A WORLD OF HEALTH: CONNECTING PEOPLE, PLACE AND PLANET

Curriculum Director: Meg O'Brien
Layout and Typography: Margaret Parker

This course could not have happened without the help of the amazing volunteers who
comprised the curriculum committee: Lisa Frack, Rebecca Friedman, Jonathan Jelen,
Sarah Menzies, Betty Shelley, Kate Rinder, Lena Rotenberg, Emily West and Atty Zschau.
They shared their time, talent, humor and wisdom to help develop this course.
Many other NWEI volunteers contributed to this effort as well, from typing and proofing,
to reviewing a draft copy. We are grateful for their support of our work.

*This publication was printed using 100% post-consumer waste, FSC certified recycled paper,
and vegetable-based inks, and is 100% process-chlorine free.*

TABLE OF

CONTENTS

INTRODUCTION

Thank you for participating in a Northwest Earth Institute discussion course. The Northwest Earth Institute is a non-profit organization working to *inspire people to take responsibility for Earth* through transformative small group dialogue. Since 1993 over 110,000 participants throughout North America have gathered in groups to explore the critical issues of our times through dialogue with others.

Recently, there has been considerable attention and debate around the topic of health, much of it focused on issues of access and coverage. We hope to broaden that conversation by bringing together people like you, to consider what "good health" really means and how we, both individually and collectively, can enjoy it.

The course begins by examining the roots of Western medicine and how it has evolved in an industrial society. It then progresses through the places where our personal health intersects with the environment — from our food and homes, to our communities and society, and finally, to our planet. At each stage we find individual actions that promote good health and in turn promote a healthier environment. These positive changes reinforce one another, since a healthier environment is a fundamental condition for sustaining human health and well-being, as well as the health of all the other species with whom we share our planet.

The course consists of six sessions, designed for group discussion. Sessions include readings, video clips, short assignments and group discussion questions. To help connect the session themes to actions you can take, you will also find a weekly EcoChallenge, a What You Can Do list, and a list of Further Readings and Resources. Please plan on spending about an hour to prepare for each meeting.

As you gather with your discussion group, we invite you to bring your own experience, critical thinking and ideas to the process. The readings are intended to invoke meaningful conversation and inspire action. We hope you will come away from this experience with an increased awareness of the connections between health and the environment and actions that you can take to promote health for your loved ones and for the Earth.

If you wish to learn more about the Northwest Earth Institute, please visit our website at www.nwei.org and sign up to receive NWEI's email updates. To support the sharing of this work with others, become a member of NWEI by making a donation at www.nwei.org/join or by completing the membership form on page 95. You may also join by contacting our office at (503) 227-2807.

The Northwest Earth Institute currently offers the following discussion courses:

- *Choices for Sustainable Living*
- *Voluntary Simplicity*
- *Menu for the Future*
- *Global Warming, Changing CO$_2$urse*
- *Sustainable Systems at Work*
- *Reconnecting with Earth*
- *Healthy Children, Healthy Planet*
- *Discovering a Sense of Place*

Special thanks to the generous individuals who made this course possible by making donations to "sponsor a page" of this discussion course book. Donor inscriptions are noted at the bottom of the pages throughout this book.

Health must be one of life's greatest joys,
as no other joy is possible without it.

— ANONYMOUS

Tips for Implementing
A World of Health:
Connecting People, Place and Planet

Thank you for your interest in the programs offered by the Northwest Earth Institute. The following tips serve as a guide as you prepare to implement *A World of Health: Connecting People, Place and Planet* in your organization or community. While this discussion guide has tremendous stand-alone value, please keep in mind it was designed to be used with others in a group dialogue setting. The following suggestions are based on NWEI's experience with facilitating small group programs since 1993.

1. The ideal group size is 8-12 participants. This ensures that each member will be able to actively participate in each discussion.

2. Host an introductory orientation meeting for participants in order to share information about the course and course process. Invite people to sign up (if participation is not required).

3. Describe the group process. One of the key benefits of participation in NWEI programs is that participants have the opportunity to facilitate sessions on a rotating basis. Most groups meet for an hour and a half for each meeting. Each session will be led by a volunteer facilitator from the group.

4. Point out the "Guidelines for the Weekly Facilitator" found on page 6. Note that NWEI programs are designed to encourage discussions inspiring behavior change. Consensus regarding content found in the articles is not the goal. Be sure to explain the role of the facilitator, using the next page as a reference point.

5. Ensure that participants have signed up for the opening and facilitating roles (using the Course Schedule form below).

6. Follow the format presented throughout the course book. Begin each session with a brief opening (described on page 6), followed by the Circle Question (provided in each session), then follow with the other discussion questions provided in each session.

You will receive the most benefit from this course if you complete all assignments and participate in each of the group discussions. If you have questions along the way, please don't hesitate to contact our support team at 503-227-2807 or email contact@nwei.org.

We trust your course experience will be of value and we appreciate your commitment to creating a more healthy future.

COURSE SCHEDULE FOR *A WORLD OF HEALTH: CONNECTING PEOPLE, PLACE AND PLANET*

This course schedule may be useful to keep track of meeting dates and of when you will be facilitating or providing the opening.

CLASS SESSION	DATE	OPENING	FACILITATING
Redefining Health			
Eating Well			
Cleaning House			
Building Healthy Communities			
Curing Consumption			
Healthy Planet, Healthy Self			

GUIDELINES

FOR FACILITATING AND OPENING

For each session of this course, one participant facilitates the discussion and one participant leads the "opening." The roles rotate each week with a different group member offering an opening and another member facilitating. This process is at the core of the Earth Institute culture — it assumes we gain our greatest insights through self-discovery and peer learning.

✦ ✦ ✦

FOR THE SESSION FACILITATOR

As facilitator for one session, your role is to stimulate and moderate the discussion. You do not need to be an expert or the most knowledgeable person about the topic.

Your role is to:

• Remind the designated person ahead of time to bring an opening.

• Begin and end on time.

• Feel free to ask the questions included in each chapter, any of the following general questions, or your own:

  – Did you have a strong reaction to any of the articles in this session?

  – What surprised you the most in this session?

  – Did you learn any new information or gain new insights from this session?

  – Do the materials in this session inspire any changes in your daily life?

• Make sure your group has time to respond to the action-oriented discussion questions about the Weekly EcoChallenge — it is a positive way to end each gathering.

• Keep discussion focused on the session's topic. A delicate balance is best — don't force the group into the questions, but don't allow the discussion to drift too far.

• Manage the group process, using the guidelines below:

A primary goal is for everyone to participate and to learn from themselves and each other. Draw out quiet participants by creating an opportunity for each person to contribute. Don't let one or two people dominate the discussion. Thank them for their opinions and then ask another person to share.

Be an active listener. You need to hear and understand what people say if you are to guide the discussion effectively. Model this for others.

The focus should be on personal reactions to the readings and ideas for taking action. The course is not for judging others' responses or problem solving. Consensus is not a goal.

FOR THE SESSION OPENING

• Bring a short opening, not more than five minutes. It should be something that expresses your personal appreciation for the natural world. Examples: a short personal story, an object or photograph that has special meaning, a poem, a visual, etc. Be creative.

• The purpose of the opening is twofold. First, it provides a transition from other activities of the day into the group discussion. Second, since the opening is personal, it allows the group to get better acquainted with you. This aspect of the course can be very rewarding.

For more information on the NWEI course model and organizing a course, see "Tips for Implementing A World of Health: Connecting People, Place and Planet" on page 5.

EVALUATION

Optional contact information:

Name_____

Address _____

Phone_____E-mail_____

❏ Please add me to your e-newsletter list.

PART 1. PLEASE FILL OUT WEEKLY, while your thoughts and opinions are fresh in your mind. We suggest removing this page to use as a bookmark as you read through the course. Rate the six sessions. If you prefer to submit this online, go to www.nwei.org/evaluation.

	POOR CHOICE			EXCELLENT	COMMENTS:
1. Redefining Health	1	2	3	4 5	
2. Eating Well	1	2	3	4 5	
3. Cleaning House	1	2	3	4 5	
4. Building Healthy Communities	1	2	3	4 5	
5. Curing Consumption	1	2	3	4 5	
6. Healthy Planet, Healthy Self	1	2	3	4 5	

Were the following materials helpful? Circle "Y" if we should use the material next time or "N" if we should replace it instead.

COMMENTS:

1. "The Diagnosis of the Unknown Physician" ....Y N
   "Beyond the Patient"..Y N
   "The Coming Age of Ecological Medicine" ....Y N
   "The Rabies Principle" ....Y N

2. Weekly EcoChallenge: Eating BPA-Free Meals................Y N
   "Buying Organic: Some Points to Consider" ....Y N
   "Pesticide Drift" ....Y N
   "The Myth of the BPA-Free Diet" ....Y N
   "Cheap Eats" ....Y N
   "The Only Way to have a Cow" ....Y N
   Video: "Teach Every Child About Food" ....Y N

3. Weekly EcoChallenge: Detoxing Your Home..................Y N
   "How to Keep Your Family Safe from Toxic Chemicals".......Y N
   "Nine Ways to Avoid Household Toxins" ....Y N
   "Bridging the Divide: It's Not Only About Taste" ....Y N
   "The Dark Side of Lawns" ....Y N
   Excerpt from *Chasing Molecules* ....Y N
   Healthy Home Assessment..Y N

4. Weekly EcoChallenge: Driving Less ....Y N
   Creating an Accessibility Map ....Y N
   "Environmental Amnesia" ....Y N
   "Our Chemical Legacy" ....Y N
   "At Risk: High-Traffic Areas".................................Y N
   Excerpt from *Big Box Swindle* ....Y N
   "Why Bikes are a Sustainable Wonder" ....Y N
   "Leave No Child Inside" ....Y N

5. Weekly EcoChallenge: Buying Less.............................Y N
   Video: "The Story of Stuff" ....Y N
   "The Rise and Fall of Consumer Cultures".................Y N
   "Simplicity and Consumption" ....Y N
   "The Plastic Killing Fields".....................................Y N
   "e-Waste: Where Does It Go".................................Y N
   "A Cure for Consumption" ....Y N
   "One Approach to Sustainability: Work Less".............Y N

6. Weekly EcoChallenge: Saving Energy ....Y N
   "Think Like an Ocean" ....Y N
   "Embedded in Nature: Human Health and Biodiversity" ......Y N
   "Climate Change and Health Vulnerabilities" ....Y N
   "Restoring Nature, Restoring Yourself".........................Y N
   "3 Bets" ....Y N
   Excerpt from *Hunting for Hope*...............................Y N

If a NWEI representative has been involved in your course, he or she will collect evaluations at the final session. If not, please send your completed evaluation to NWEI, 107 SE Washington, Suite 235, Portland, OR 97214.

PART 2. PLEASE COMPLETE AT END OF COURSE.

Has the course made an impact on you?   Yes No   Please describe how._____
_____
_____
_____

Please list other articles or books that should be included in the course. Identify URLs or chapter(s)/page(s) and the session where they should be included. _____
_____
_____
_____

Were the session activities and Weekly EcoChallenges beneficial? Why or why not? _____
_____
_____
_____

What has been the most valuable aspect of this course? _____
_____
_____
_____

REDEFINING HEALTH

*Good health lies in recognizing that each of us is part of a wider web of life.
When the web is healthy, we are more likely to be healthy… Just as the knee bone is connected to the thigh bone,
humans and environmental health are inseparable.*

— Kenny Ausubel, founder of Bioneers

SESSION GOALS

- To examine our personal beliefs and attitudes about health

- To examine modern medicine's approach to health and the environment

- To explore the tenets of ecological medicine

- To become familiar with the precautionary principle

SESSION BACKGROUND

Good health is something we all strive for, but what do we really mean when we talk about it, and how might we go about creating the conditions that foster it? This session explores how we define health and how that understanding informs our individual and collective well-being. The readings included here propose a fundamental shift from the current perspective to a more integrated view of health; that is to say, one that understands health as a dynamic relationship between humans and the environments they live within.

In the first reading, "The Diagnosis of the Unknown Physician," environmental lawyer, Carolyn Raffensperger, offers several definitions of health, as well as her own prescription for addressing the health issues of the 21st Century.

In the next reading, "Beyond the Patient," Lee Thirer traces the roots of modern medicine back to Hippocrates' treatise *On Airs, Waters, and Places*, noting its emphasis on ecology. Thirer describes a growing number of practitioners who, recognizing how far modern medicine has strayed from this ecological view, have become part of an "ecological medicine" movement. Kenny Ausubel explores this idea further in "The Coming Age of Ecological Medicine." He introduces the precautionary principle as a primary tool of ecological medicine, a concept which is illustrated in the final reading, "The Rabies Principle," by Sandra Steingraber.

Circle Question

To what extent do you believe that environmental factors contribute to health problems?

Circle questions should move quickly — each member responds briefly without questions or comments from others. Facilitator guidelines are on page 6.

SUGGESTED DISCUSSION QUESTIONS

1. In the first reading, Carolyn Raffensperger offers several definitions of health. Which resonates with you the most? Explain.

2. In your opinion, is the Hippocratic Oath still paramount today?

3. What would your ideal doctor's appointment look like? Would you go to a physician who practiced "ecological medicine" if one was available to you? Why or why not?

4. In "The Coming Age of Ecological Medicine," Kenny Ausubel describes some of the medical-waste problems associated with current medical practices. Can you think of more ecologically sound practices that your health care practitioners could adopt?

5. Why aren't environmental issues addressed in most medical schools? Should they be?

6. Which makes more sense to you, the European adoption of the precautionary principle or the American inclination to assume that something is safe unless proven to be harmful?

7. When is the current "risk paradigm" acceptable and unacceptable to you? Where do you draw the line?

8. Kenny Ausubel describes how some governments support sustainable practices, such as a taxes on pesticides, or paying farmers to grow organically in watersheds. What would it take to do that in the United States?

9. Sandra Steingraber provides reasons why public health officials treat rabies differently than environmental pollutants known to be harmful to our health. Which of her reasons sounds most compelling to you?

Weekly EcoChallenge

In the next five sessions, look here for your group's Weekly EcoChallenge. The challenges are tied to the session themes, providing an opportunity to put your learning into action. A week before each meeting, be sure to see what the suggested action is and determine a realistic but challenging way to incorporate it into your life for a week. At the next meeting you will have an opportunity to share your struggles and successes with your group.

To find out more about NWEI's annual EcoChallenge event, visit.www.ecochallenge.org.

SUGGESTED READINGS AND RESOURCES

ORGANIZATIONS

Silent Spring Institute: researches the link between the chemicals and toxins that have made their way into our environment and breast cancer. www.silentspring.org

Science and Environmental Health Network has been the leading proponent in the United States of the Precautionary Principle as a new basis for environmental and public health policy. www.sehn.org

ARTICLES

Please go to the Northwest Earth Institute website (www.nwei.org) for the most current list of articles relating to this session.

BOOKS

Alternative Medicine: The Definitive Guide (2nd Edition) by Burton Goldberg, John W. Andersen and Larry Triviera. Four hundred of the world's leading alternative physicians have contributed safe, affordable, and effective remedies for more than 200 medical conditions ranging from common health problems like allergies, asthma, and obesity to serious illnesses like cancer, heart disease, and AIDS.

FILMS/DOCUMENTARIES

Living Downstream is a documentary based on the acclaimed book by ecologist Sandra Steingraber. The film follows Steingraber during one pivotal year as she travels across North America, working to break the silence about cancer and its environmental links.

THE DIAGNOSIS OF THE UNKNOWN PHYSICIAN

By Carolyn Raffensperger

According to an old story told by Sun Tsu at the beginning of *The Art of War*, a lord of ancient China once asked his physician, a member of a family of healers, which family member was the most skilled at medicine. The famous physician replied, "My eldest brother is the most skilled since he sees the spirit of sickness and removes it before it takes shape, so his name does not get out of the house. My elder brother cures sickness when it is still extremely minute, so his name does not get out of the neighborhood." The greatest physician was unknown because he prevented disease rather than having to cure it.

✦ ✦ ✦

I have the remarkable fortune of having great genes. Both my parents are alive, well and unusually rascally for Midwesterners. My Dad was in his late 60s when he sailed across the Atlantic and back. He published a novel last year under a pseudonym (so don't look for it using my name) and regularly paddles out into the ocean in his homemade sea kayak. My Mom was in her mid-70s when she got a new job on the upper Peninsula of Michigan, moved into a log cabin and took up snow-shoeing and nature photography. They have no history of cancer, diabetes, or cardio-vascular problems. Alas, my parents' medical histories aren't going to be much help in predicting what I will live with as I age

and what I will die of. All the trends in things like cancer, Alzheimer's, diabetes, and Parkinson's suggest that I along with my age cohort are going to be sicker longer and die after lingering, debilitating illnesses.

What's going on? Basically our diseases are corollaries of our civilization. As Rene Dubos said, "each type of society has diseases peculiar to itself — indeed, . . . each civilization creates its own diseases." Our bodies reflect the interaction of our genes with the manifestations of our civilization — the built, social and natural environments. In fifty years we've fundamentally altered all of these systems. We get less exercise, we eat nutritionally-suspect food and we've filled our world with toxic chemicals. . . .Where are we headed given this trajectory? Here are my four predictions on the future of human health.

1) We will see more chronic diseases such as asthma, diabetes, and Alzheimer's. The reason is that we have a whole long list of stressors like nutritionally deficient diets, inadequate exercise, and air pollution, all of which lead to oxidative stress and inflammation — the biological mechanisms for disease.

2) Diseases that make people fundamentally anti-social will affect a much larger population. These illnesses include autism, Alzheimer's, and mental illness. These diseases are rising now in the population and render people unable to function within their families and communities.

3) We will suffer from an increased number of rapidly changing infectious, zoonotic pandemics (think swine flu, bird flu, hemorrhagic viruses.) because climate change,

modern transportation, and industrial agriculture are disrupting ecologies, setting up the conditions for rapidly evolving bacteria, funguses and bacteria that use multiple species as hosts. In addition, we are moving people and stuff around the planet at an ever increasing rate. Infectious agents are hitching rides and zipping around the planet in cargo ships and airplanes.

4) Subtle, difficult to diagnose malaises like chronic fatigue, fibromyalgia, and suppressed immune systems will become the norm. Patients will exhibit multi-factorial, complex symptoms that defy categorization.

If we wanted to alter this course, where would we start? We'd start with decent definitions of health because how we define it determines how we maintain health and cure disease.

Wendell Berry defines health as membership — membership in the community of humans and membership in the Earth community. "Can our present medical industry produce an adequate definition of health? My own guess is that it cannot do so. Like industrial agriculture, industrial medicine has depended increasingly on specialist methodology, mechanical technology, and chemicals; thus, its point of reference has become more and more its own technical prowess and less and less the health of creatures and habitats." Berry later says, "this, plainly, is a view of health that is severely reductive. It is, to begin with, almost fanatically individualistic. The body is seen as a defective or potentially defective machine, singular, solitary, and displaced, without love, solace, or pleasure. Its health excludes unhealthy cigarettes but does not exclude unhealthy food, water, and air. One may presumably be healthy in a disintegrated family or community or in a destroyed or poisoned ecosystem."

A related definition to Berry's idea of membership comes from Aldo Leopold who defined health as the capacity for self-renewal. Leopold was referring to land but it applies equally well to the individual. Leopold means that health is an intrinsic and internal biological process, not a static quality. It is the process of re-membering our communities.

Sun Tsu's unknown physician must have been working with similar definitions of health in order to prevent the diseases of his day. Today, I imagine he would write a prescription to restore the Earth's resilience, and repair the social systems to alleviate the debilitating stresses of poverty, racism and hunger, and create built environments that nurtured living beings.

This article was posted on December 10, 2009, Science and Environmental Health Network webpage, www.sehn.org. Carolyn Raffensperger is executive director of the Science & Environmental Health Network, www.sehn.org. As an environmental lawyer she specializes in the fundamental changes in law and policy necessary for the protection and restoration of public health and the environment.

BEYOND THE PATIENT

By Lee Thirer

Before Hippocrates, health was a supernatural affair. Exorcists and priests charmed money from the dying. Snakes squirmed beneath sickbeds: Sacred dogs licked fatal wounds. Pilgrims dozed within shrines, awaiting divine visitations, and dreamed of magical cures at places like the temple hill at Cos, where the mastermind of Western medicine — born on the island around 460 BC — rooted his revolution in ecology. Though few who now benefit from modern medicine remember, its creator overthrew the order of the gods with one simple mandate: that the physician seek truth only in the natural world, in the study of air, water, soil, and climate — in the study of the body within its ecosystem.

"From these things," Hippocrates commanded in his treatise *On Airs, Waters, and Places*, "he must proceed to investigate everything else."

Hippocrates taught that nature was the doctor, the doctor its aide. Studying the interchange of the internal and the external, a Hippocratic healer paid careful attention to food, exercise, and the ways the waters and the climates acted on the four humors — blood, phlegm, and yellow and black biles, each associated with a particular temperament. By trusting and helping nature, the great healer, to maintain health, Hippocrates' students sought to provide preventive care over a lifetime. Only after nature had begun to fail would the doctor prescribe treatments that would, in Hippocrates' words, "help, or at least do no harm."

For the first time in millennia, however, nature itself is so unwell that doctors cannot fulfill their ancient duties. Twenty-six centuries of medical innovations cannot now protect the patient from the wider world, with its modern stresses and toxicity. And even if they could, modern doctors are focused elsewhere. "We shouldn't pretend that clinical medicine is really doing primary prevention," says Ted Schettler, science director of the non-profit Science and Environmental Health Network, "because it's not — and it's not particularly interested in it."

Recognizing these shortcomings, a network of doctors, nurses, and other health practitioners, loosely affiliated in an "ecological medicine" movement, have begun not only to re-emphasize prevention but also to adopt a broader definition of preventive care.

"Our focus has always been on taking care of the immediate patient in front of us," says Calista Hunter, an internist in Lafayette, California. "That's all we really focus on. My hope is that physicians, as they become more environmentally aware, will realize that they can help a lot more people by addressing environmental issues that influence their patients."

Hunter serves on the board of the Berkeley-based Teleosis Institute, one of a half-dozen U.S. nonprofits devoted to ecological medicine. Teleosis has two main goals: preventing the environmental causes of harm and stopping health care itself from contributing to them. …"We're doing continuing medical education lectures at a lot of local hospitals," says Hunter. "And I have found that every time I talk to a physician about environmental issues related to their specialty, people are responsive." Each specialist knows of some discrete environmental source of illness, Hunter says — an ear, nose, and throat doctor may bring up concerns about noise pollution; an oncologist may talk about disposal of medications in hospice care.

Casual disposal of medication is a major target for proponents of ecological medicine. When a hospice patient dies, weeks' worth of medicines are often flushed down the toilet and into the watershed, joining various other toxic health-care byproducts and excreted pharmaceuticals. A 2006 study in the journal *Environmental Science and Technology* found that a mixture of thirteen such substances inhibits the growth of human embryonic cells at environmental-exposure levels. Studies have also linked estrogen-related pharmaceutical waste to endocrine disruption in animals, including feminization of male fish. In 2001, the U.S. Geological Survey reported finding medicines in every one of eighty waterways tested nationwide.

"Medications have to go somewhere after people take them and excrete them," explains Sue Stone, a family physician based in Fresno, California. "The chemical byproducts seep back into the environment and it just adds to the chemical load."

Those byproducts are clear testaments to the fact that there is no "away" — that the external is the internal and that interconnectedness is a profound biological truth. It is the idea upon which medicine itself is founded; not even the most innovative or preventive treatments can shield the body from its ecosystem. Indeed, the most common waterborne medications are testaments to an unhealthy habitat: acetaminophen and codeine bespeak the strains of modern life and its reliance on palliatives. And diltiazem, a blood-pressure medication, bears witness to epidemic psychosocial stress, the sedentary and solitary nature of a sprawl-divided society, a sick food system, even noise pollution.

If it is to meet its ethical obligations, says nurse Anna Gilmore Hall, executive director of the nonprofit Health Care Without Harm, the medical sector must be "a driver of change, not only modifying our practices and activities but helping other sectors in society to identify how they can change." Gilmore's organization, another proponent of ecological medicine, has led a successful campaign against the incineration of medical waste, including the polyvinyl chloride products whose burning emits cancer-causing dioxins.

Much as Hippocratic doctrine rooted medicine in duty to the whole patient, the nascent ecological medicine movement seeks to treat the whole of society as its patient. New York City integrative oncologist and environmental activist Mitch Gaynor says that the ancient mandate "first, do no harm" should require health-care practitioners to educate industry and demand that all chemical manufacturers prove product safety. The larger goal should be "changing consciousness in individuals and institutions."

That shift in consciousness has begun to manifest in medical institutions like Oakland-based Kaiser Permanente, the nation's largest nonprofit health care system. In an August 2006 pilot project, Kaiser began working with about a dozen low-income California farmers who do not spray pesticides; they now supply fruits and vegetables for patient meal-trays in nineteen Kaiser facilities in northern California. According to Kaiser's environmental stewardship manager, Lynn Garske, the project is opening markets to farmers and workers who themselves often can't afford high-quality food and health coverage — people who would "end up presenting at our facilities or even our sister facilities and other hospitals in the area," she says. And in supporting the farmers, the project also supports

> "Those byproducts are clear testaments to the fact that there is no 'away' — that the external is the internal and that interconnectedness is a profound biological truth."

conscientious agriculture, nourishing nature so nature will nourish patients.

This collaboration is an example of what Schettler calls a "new ecology of institutions." But it will be hard-pressed to make much headway as long as the economy is propelled by a pre-Hippocratic assumption: that the primary purpose of medicine is to cure diseases. The medical sector currently accounts for more than 16 percent of the gross domestic product and is expected to grow to 20 percent in the next decade. And there are those, says Schettler, who want to see it grow further still. But the fundamental twenty-first-century choice, as he sees it — between health care and disease care — will hinge on acceptance of an ethical mandate as old and vital as medicine itself: "As we decide how to live in the world, what to do, and how to make changes, first — do no harm."

Published in the March/April 2007 issue of Orion magazine. Lee Thirer is a freelance writer living in the San Francisco Bay Area.

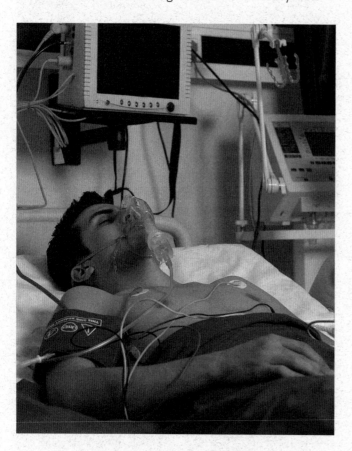

THE COMING AGE OF ECOLOGICAL MEDICINE

By Kenny Ausubel

Among the many immigrants who arrived in New York City in the summer of 1999, none made a name for itself more quickly than West Nile fever. Traced to a virus spread by mosquitoes, the disease had never been seen in this country, or even in the Western Hemisphere. It first struck birds, then people, killing seven and sickening dozens more.

The city hoped to control it by killing the mosquitoes with malathion, a pesticide chemically related to nerve gas. Though many protested, Mayor Rudolph Giuliani insisted the spraying was perfectly safe.

Within months, scientists at the U.S. Environmental Protection Agency were debating just how wrong the mayor had been. The EPA was on the verge of declaring malathion a "likely" human carcinogen when its manufacturer protested. The EPA backed off, saying malathion posed no documented threat, though some in the agency continued to insist the dangers were being downplayed. More suspicion was raised upon news of a massive die-off among lobsters in Long Island Sound near New York. Malathion is known to kill lobsters and other marine life, but officials denied the connection.

Though no direct causal link can yet be drawn, some infectious-disease experts say anomalous outbreaks such as West Nile may be tied to human impacts on the environment, including climate change and the destruction of natural habitats. As noted by Dr. Paul R. Epstein, associate director of the Center for Health and the Global Environment at Harvard Medical School, "West Nile is getting veterinarians and doctors and biologists to sit down at the same table." What they are unraveling is a complex knot linking human health and the state of the natural world.

Welcome to a preview of the health issues awaiting us in the 21st century. Indeed, we're already living at a time when vast social and biological forces are interacting in complex ways — and with unpredictable impacts. War, famine, and ecological damage have caused great human disruptions, which in turn have transformed tuberculosis, AIDS, and other modern plagues into global pandemics.

Even more disturbing, many of our efforts to fight disease today are themselves symptoms of a deeper illness. Spraying an urban area with a substance whose health effects remain unknown is one glaring example, but there are many others: Think of certain compounds used in chemotherapy that more often kill than cure. Or the 100,000 people who die in hospitals every year from drugs that are *properly prescribed*. Or the many IV bags and other plastic medical products that release dioxin into the air when they are burned.

That last example contributes to perhaps the most heartbreaking metaphor of our environmental abuse and its unforeseen consequences — the discovery that human mother's milk is among the most toxic human foods, laced with dioxin, a confirmed carcinogen, and other chemical contaminants. All these cases suggest our culture's deep dependence on synthetic chemicals, and our long refusal to acknowledge how profoundly they've disrupted our ecological systems.

Thanks to George Rives

There's a widespread sense that mainstream medicine is blind to this reality, and is even part of the problem. This growing disillusion, coupled with the fact that high-tech medicine costs too much and often doesn't work, has led to a widespread public search for alternatives. One result is the rise of complementary medicine, which combines the best of modern health care with other approaches. Add the immense new interest in traditional healing methods, herbs, and other natural remedies and you get a sense of how much the health-care paradigm has changed over the past 30 years.

What I see happening is a deeper shift that all these approaches are edging us toward, even if we don't fully realize it yet. It's a new understanding of health and illness that has begun to move away from treating only the individual. Instead, good health lies in recognizing that each of us is part of a wider web of life. When the web is healthy, we are more likely to be healthy. But the environmental illnesses we see more and more of these days — rising cancer rates spring to mind — are constant reminders that the web is not healthy. How did we reach this tragic place? And more to the point, where do we go from here?

The first step toward a healthier future, I believe, lies in ecological medicine. Pioneered by a global movement of concerned scientists, doctors, and many others, ecological medicine is a loosely shared philosophy based on advancing public health by improving the environment. Its central idea is that industrial civilization has made a basic error in acting as if humans are apart from, rather than a part of, nature. Just as the knee bone is connected to the thigh bone, human and environmental health are inseparable.

And in a biosphere that is rampantly toxic and woefully depleted, a mounting number of our health problems can only be understood as part of a larger pattern. Ecological medicine could well emerge as a force for dramatic cultural change. It proposes to reshape how industrial civilization operates, in part by redefining the role that the public plays in making the decisions that affect all life on earth.

Simply stated, improving human health is inextricably linked to ecological well-being. The interconnectedness of all life is a fundamental biological truth. What's more, all life is under threat. There simply is no "elsewhere" to dump the hazardous by-products of industrial society. Eliminating them from our production systems is the only solution, and a well-informed public is crucial to realizing it. ...
Here are some basic tenets of ecological medicine:

- The first goal of medicine is to establish the conditions for health and wholeness, thus preventing disease and illness. The second goal is to cure.

- The earth is also the physician's client. The patient under the physician's care is one part of the earth.

- Humans are part of a local eco-system. Following the ecopsychological insight that a disturbed ecosystem can make people mentally ill, a disturbed ecosystem can surely make people physically ill.

- Medicine should not add to the illnesses of humans or the planet. Medical practices themselves should not damage other species or the ecosystem.

The main tool for putting these ideals into practice, ecological healers say, is what they call the precautionary principle. ...The precautionary principle basically argues that science and industry must fully assess the impact of their activities before they impose them upon the public and the environment. Societies around the world have begun to incorporate some version of the principle into law, hoping to rein in bioengineering and other new technologies. That science should objectively prove the safety of its own inventions might seem like common sense, but that's not how most science operates today.

For decades, the scientific and medical community has accepted that a certain amount of pollution and disease is just the price we have to pay for modern life. This is called the "risk paradigm," and it essentially means that it is society's burden to prove that new technologies and industrial processes are harmful, usually one chemical or technology at a time. The risk paradigm assumes that there are "acceptable" levels of contamination the earth and our bodies can supposedly assimilate. ....

There is a global effort afoot today to replace the risk paradigm with the precautionary principle, which is based on a recognition of science's limits in fully predicting consequences and possible harm. The precautionary principle acknowledges that all life is interconnected. It shifts the burden of proof (and liability) to the parties promoting potentially harmful technologies, and limits their use to experiments until they are proven truly safe.

The idea is not new — a version of it first appeared in U.S. law back in 1958 in the Delaney Amendment, which governed pesticide residues in food and set standards for environmental impact statements. Nor is it radical. At its essence, the principle harks back to grandma's admonitions that "an ounce of prevention is worth a pound of cure," that we're "better safe than sorry."

The model is already used, in theory, for the drug industry, which is legally bound to prove drugs safe and effective prior to their use. Critics call it anti-scientific; they say it limits trade and stifles innovation.

Ecological medicine advocates disagree.

"The precautionary principle actually sheds a bright light on science," says Dr. Ted Schettler, science director of Science and Environmental Health Network (SEHN). "It doesn't tell us what to do, but it does tell you what to look at." Germany and Sweden have incorporated the principle into certain environmental policies. The United Nations Biosafety Protocol includes it as part of new guidelines for regulating trade in genetically modified products, its first appearance in an international treaty.

As people and their governments face ever more complex scientific decisions, the precautionary principle can serve as what some have called an "insurance policy against our own ignorance." After all, we can't even predict next week's weather or the economy a year out, much less the unfathomable complexity of living systems.

The Hippocratic oath tells doctors to "First, do no harm," yet our medical practices often pose serious environmental threats. In 1994, for instance, the EPA reported that medical waste incinerators were the biggest source of dioxin air pollution in the United States. Dioxin finds its way into our food and accumulates in our fat; it's been linked to neurological damage in fetuses. Even a simple thermometer contains mercury, another potentially deadly neurotoxin.

The medical-waste problem does not stop there. Along with generating radioactive waste from various treatments, the medical industry is now the source of a new peril: pharmaceutical pollution. Creatures living in lakes and rivers appear to be at special risk as antibiotics, estrogen, birth-control pills, painkillers, and other drugs find their way into the waste stream. Fish are already affected; intersex mutations (showing both male and female characteristics) have been reported in various species around the world. But humans are not immune. The war on drugs may soon take on a new meaning as entire populations are subjected to constant low doses of pharmaceuticals in the water supply.

Groups like Health Care Without Harm (www.noharm. org) have made it their mission to halt or curb such damaging medical practices, especially the use of mercury thermometers and the industry's reliance on burning its waste. …

Ecological medicine suggests first doing no harm to the environment, then going further, creating a medical practice that itself minimizes harm. Like virtually all earlier healing traditions, it emphasizes prevention, strengthening the organism and the environment to avoid illness in the first place. Ancient Chinese healers, for instance, expected compensation only if their clients remained well, not when they got sick.

But an ecological approach to healing also looks to deeper tenets embedded in nature and how it operates. Again, the new vision reveals itself to be in many ways an old one. It borrows from the insights of indigenous healing traditions, many of which are now being confirmed by modern science — including the fact that nature has an extraordinary and mysterious capacity for self-repair.

However resilient the biosphere may be, it's crucial to understand that the planet's basic life support systems are in serious decline. From climate change to plummeting biodiversity to gargantuan quantities of toxic wastes, the ecological stresses are reaching dangerous thresholds. Much of the damage can be traced to the 20th century's three most destructive technologies: petrochemicals, nuclear energy, and genetic engineering. …

In addition to instructing healers first to do no harm, Hippocrates also instructed them in a lesser-known passage to "revere the healing force of nature." For years, that's been my quest: working with nature to heal nature. I founded the Bioneers Conference in 1990 to bring together people exploring ways of doing this — biological pioneers from many cultures and disciplines, and from all walks of life. All had peered deep into the heart of the earth's own living systems to understand what we can learn from 3.8 billion years of evolution. Their common purpose was to heal the earth.

Their basic question: How would nature do it? They were all using their knowledge of living systems to devise solutions to our most pressing environmental and societal problems. I now realize these people are modern healers, too.

As their work repeatedly illustrates, we already have many of the technologies we need to retool our industrial system. Many of the bioneers show how we can replace existing industrial practices with sustainable alternatives that run on clean, renewable energy sources. Government has a role to play in this process too. Several years ago Sweden imposed a steep tax on pesticides, a measure that greatly reduced their use. Europe recently banned four antibiotics from animal feed. On the other side of the equation, governments are using tax subsidies to promote sustainable technologies such as chlorine-free paper production and organic farming. The city of Munich pays German farmers to grow organically in the watershed that supplies drinking water. …

The ethic of preventing harm as seen in both environmental protection and ecological medicine will continue to spread, but what about existing messes? Many treatment methods modeled on living systems have shown dramatic capacities for bioremediation — that is, for detoxifying land, air, and water.

Visionary biologist John Todd's "living machines" mimic natural ecologies by utilizing bacteria, fungi, plants, fish, and mammals to purify water and industrial "wastes." The work of mycologist Paul Stamets has shown that fungi can help digest diesel spills and even chemical and biological weapons components.

Similar success stories are found across many fields. By looking to the principles of ecological healing to restore the earth and ourselves, we create not only the conditions for individual health, but also the basis for healthy societies and robust economies.

By restoring the earth, we restore ourselves.

Published in *Utne* , May 25, 2001. Kenny Ausubel is the founder of the Bioneers Conference, www.bioneers.org.

THE RABIES PRINCIPLE

By Sandra Steingraber

The finest description of the precautionary principle that I've ever heard came from David Gee of the European Environment Agency in a speech before a convocation of environmental ministers in Belgium. After arguing that benefit of the doubt should be granted to public health rather than to the things that threaten it, Gee said that precaution helps us avoid, during times of uncertainty, the construction of "pipelines of unstoppable consequences." Gee's remarks were met with stout applause.

On this side of the Atlantic, "precautionary principle" occupies the same rhetorical space as "socialized medicine." They're words best avoided in mixed company. Even the principle's U.S. torchbearer, the Alliance for a Healthy Tomorrow, no longer uses the phrase in its name.

And yet, whatever you want to call a spade, the precautionary principle is already embedded in at least one corner of our environmental health system, as I learned when my children discovered a bat in their bedroom.

I had sent the kids upstairs to put on pajamas. When they reappeared, claiming an animal was under the bed, I pointed the way back to their room. "Pajamas. Now."

Within minutes they were at my desk again. "Mama, we think you should come." An electronic device of some kind was ringing. It occurred to me that we didn't have any toys that sounded like that. The kids solemnly followed me upstairs. Piercing bleeps came from everywhere and nowhere all at once. Like a tape loop used to disorient the enemy. Like the ring tone from hell.

I didn't think to ask Faith and Elijah to leave the room. I just started tearing it apart. The beds. The bookshelf. The toy box. Finally, I dismantled the registers, and there it was inside the guts of the baseboard heater. Coppery fur. A greasy face. Ugly. Finally, I noticed the folded umbrellas of its wings, and a Latin name scrolled into my mind — *Eptesicus fuscus*, the big brown bat. It scrabbled along a pipe. Without the faceplate to create a resonating chamber, the volume of its vocalizations dropped to a series of pitiful twangs, like the plucked string of an unplugged electric guitar.

I ordered the kids out of the room, shut the door, and stuffed a towel under it.

In upstate New York, 2 percent of big brown bats are infected with rabies.

I knew that if I failed to capture this one, my son and daughter would be compelled to undergo rabies vaccinations, in accordance with Centers for Disease Control guidelines. Bats have razors for teeth. Their bites can be undetectable. And, although the odds are 98 percent that any given bat is rabies-free, rabies is a disease with a 100 percent fatality rate.

I squatted in front of the disassembled heating register and devised a plan. What I needed was a long-sleeved shirt, a yogurt container, and leather gloves. But these were all located in different parts of the house, and I didn't want to leave my chirping intruder while I gathered the tools for its arrest. Through the door, I asked the seven year old to bring me the phone book. On the inside cover, alongside the numbers for the sheriff, fire department, and suicide counseling, was the after-hours number for the Rabies Prevention Hotline. I asked the four year old to bring me the phone. After two rings, a live person from the county health department answered. And with that phone call, a well-oiled public health apparatus swung into motion.

Within fifteen minutes, a wildlife removal specialist was standing next to me. Within another fifteen minutes the bat was inside a bucket in my freezer. By morning, its frozen corpse was in the hands of a pathologist. Twenty-four hours later, the head of the county's rabies prevention program called me.

The bat was rabid.

I needed to come to county health for an immediate interview. During that conversation, I was asked if the children had been alone in the room with the bat. I learned that a four year old is on the cusp of what's considered old enough to be a reliable narrator about whether direct contact has occurred. I was told that the decision to undergo the vaccination series was up to me. I was encouraged to decide swiftly. The initial shots needed to be given within seventy-two hours of exposure. The remaining four shots were given over twenty-eight days, according to

---

DRUGS IN OUR WATER: WHAT CAN I DO?

- Dispose of unused or unwanted medications at take-back sites

- Do NOT dispose of any medication down the toilet or in the trash

- Purchase drugs in small amounts, limiting expired medications

- Ask for medications with low environmental impact

- Encourage your health provider to take back unused and expired drugs

- Commit to health and wellness strategies to reduce your reliance on medications

- Choose meat and poultry raised without hormones and antibiotics

Source: Teleosis Institute, an educational nonprofit organization devoted to reducing the environmental impact of health care through sustainable medical practices. www.teleosis.org

Thanks to Connie and Fred Erickson

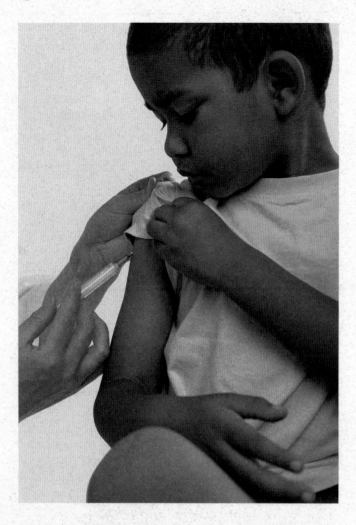

Or even: Look, we don't know if you have been exposed, but we are removing environmental carcinogens from your neighborhood because we want to err on the side of caution.

The difference between bladder cancer and rabies is not one of scientific certainty. We have as much evidence that arsenic, say, causes bladder cancer as that the rabies virus causes a fatal form of encephalitis. The difference between bladder cancer and rabies is one of what physicians call disease specificity. If I forgo a rabies vaccination and, weeks later, am sucked down the pipeline of unstoppable consequences, we'll all know what killed me. If I go on to die of bladder cancer, we won't know if it was the arsenic in the drinking water or exposure to some other carcinogen.

There are other differences between bats and chemical toxicants that help explain why our public health system takes a precautionary approach to one and a risk approach to the other. To look into the eyes of a rabid animal is to confront a visible danger. To watch your children climb a wood play structure — even knowing that the wood is suffused with leachable arsenic — is not. To remove bat roosts from one's attic — as we have subsequently done — is met with silence on the part of the bats. To remove arsenic-treated play structures from one's community nursery school — as I have attempted to do — is not met with silence by their manufacturers. Believe me.

Back at home, I conducted some interviews of my own. Faith claimed that she never saw the bat when she was alone in the room with it. She only heard it. Elijah gave me a different story — "The bat flew around and landed on my hand. It was carrying a tiny . . . GUN!" — and I learned why the CDC considers the bat reports of young children unreliable.

We had the shots. Our insurance company paid. And so my children and I were afforded 100 percent protection against an environmental disease we may or may not have been exposed to. And I could go back to work investigating environmental diseases — cancer, birth defects, asthma, learning disabilities — and their known and suspected contributors — pesticides, solvents, soot, heavy metals — to which we are all exposed but for which no emergency hotline numbers appear in our phone books and no animals bleat SOS signals from the walls of our homes.

a strict schedule. If I decided to go forward, county health would make all the arrangements. My upcoming lecture at the University of Montana? No problem. County health would arrange to send serum there. It would be waiting for me when I got off the plane. Oh, and by the way, he added, if your insurance does not reimburse, the county will pick up the cost of the vaccination series — which is several thousand dollars per person — because "we don't want anyone making this decision on the basis of money. We want to err on the side of caution here."

Those words were so amazing to me that I asked him to say that last part again. I'm a cancer survivor with enough outstanding medical debt that I was almost prevented from obtaining a mortgage for our house. In my whole medicalized life, no one has ever said to me: Look, we don't want you to forgo a cancer screening because of financial worries, and so the government will guarantee payment.

Published in the September/October 2007 issue of *Orion*. www.orionmagazine.org. Sandra Steingraber is a biologist, author, and cancer survivor who currently makes her home in Ithaca, New York. Her most acclaimed work, *Living Downstream*, details the links between cancer and toxins in the environment.

As you complete the weekly readings, please remember to fill out the course evaluation on page 7 or go to www.nwei.org/evaluation. Your comments will help NWEI improve the course. Thank you.

EATING WELL

The interesting thing I learned was that if you're really concerned about your health, the best decisions for your health turn out to be the best decisions for the farmer and the best decisions for the environment — and that there is no contradiction there.

— MICHAEL POLLAN, AUTHOR, *THE OMNIVORE'S DILEMMA*

SESSION GOALS

• **To examine the impact of the industrial food system on personal, collective and ecological health**

• **To explore the hidden costs of "cheap" food**

• **To examine the health impacts of food packaging**

• **To identify ways of reducing BPA in our diets**

SESSION BACKGROUND

Most people agree that eating well is a foundation of good health. Yet many of our decisions are now focused on *avoiding* foods that might be harmful to ourselves and our planet. How did we arrive at this point where food, which sustains us, has become something to fear? Several of the readings in this session point to the industrial food system that has transformed the American diet and landscape over the last half century. The global food system has not only changed the eating habits of Americans, it has contributed to what many call a health crisis. The readings that follow provide insights into health issues stemming from the American diet, and offer alternatives to restore our bodies and our planet.

In "Buying Organic? Some Points to Consider," Julie Deardroff lays out the basic differences between organic and conventional farming methods and their implications for our health and the environment. The impact of pesticides on those closest to them — farm workers and their families — is explored further in "Pesticide Drift" by Rebecca Clarren.

In "The Myth of the BPA-free diet," Kat Kerlin describes the current debate around plastics in food packaging and her attempts to rid them from her diet. In an excerpt from *Cheap: The High Price of Discount Culture*, Ellen Ruppell Shell peels back layers of the global food system to uncover serious food safety concerns. In "The Only Way to Have a Cow," Bill McKibben connects a meat-based diet to many Western health problems and to global climate change. Finally, celebrity chef Jamie Oliver takes his crusade against obesity and the American diet to West Virginia in a TED Talks video clip.

Circle Question

To what extent are you willing to change your diet to improve your health? Environmental health?

Circle questions should move quickly — each member responds briefly without questions or comments from others. Facilitator guidelines are on page 6.

SUGGESTED DISCUSSION QUESTIONS

1. Based on the readings, are you changing your shopping list? What influences your shopping choices most: price, convenience, packaging, personal health, treatment of animals, environmental concerns?

2. What safety concerns, if any, do you have about the food you consume? What changes can you make? Explain.

3. How often do you think of farm workers' health or the environment when you buy produce?

4. According to Bill McKibben, "industrial livestock production is essentially indefensible." What's your opinion?

5. Does the packaging of the food you buy matter to you?

6. Should the U.S. government be regulating BPA in food packaging? Why or why not?

7. What would it take to convince Americans to eat more healthfully? What are the barriers?

8. Briefly, share what you learned from your Weekly EcoChallenge. It's okay to say you've not completed this week's EcoChallenge. Your group can offer suggestions on making progress in this area and you can try it at another time.

Weekly EcoChallenge: Eating BPA-Free Meals

Choose a realistic but challenging way to reduce BPA in your diet. For example, plan meals for a day in which you eliminate all packaging with BPA from your diet. Eating fresh foods, for example, is a healthy way to avoid toxic packaging. Take it a step further: When choosing fruits and veggies, buy organic when pesticide loads are highest. Take it further and plan a whole week!

To find out more about NWEI's annual EcoChallenge event, visit www.ecochallenge.org.

SUGGESTED READINGS AND RESOURCES

ORGANIZATIONS

Center for Food Safety works to protect human health and the environment by curbing the proliferation of harmful food production technologies and by promoting organic and other forms of sustainable agriculture. www.centerforfoodsafety.org

Organic Consumers Association is an online and grassroots public interest organization campaigning for health, justice, and sustainability . Its e-newsletter (www.organicconsumers.org/organicbytes.cfm), provides information on biotechnology/GMOs, Farm Bill, organic labeling practices, and much more.

ARTICLES

Please go to the Northwest Earth Institute website (www.nwei.org) for the most current list of articles relating to this session.

BOOKS

FoodFight: The Citizen's Guide to a Food and Farm Bill by Daniel Imhoff (2007). Imhoff deconstructs the Farm Bill and what it means for Americans in terms of health, cost and food security.

The Food Revolution: How Your Diet Can Help Save Your Life and Our World, by John Robbins (2001). Robbins argues for the merits of vegetarianism as a way to help stop global warming, curb hunger, avoid genetically modified foods, and, overall, live a healthier life.

In Defense of Food: An Eater's Manifesto, by Michael Pollan (2008). Pollan argues that much of what we are eating today is not really "real" food and advocates we shift our focus back to a diet of less excess and more plants.

FILMS/DOCUMENTARIES

Food Inc. In this documentary, filmmaker Robert Kenner lifts the veil on our nation's food industry, exposing the highly mechanized underbelly that goes unseen by the American consumer.

King Corn. This documentary follows the efforts of two friends as they work to produce a large crop of corn, the real driving force behind America's food industry.

BUYING ORGANIC: SOME POINTS TO CONSIDER

By Julie Deardorff

Some consumers are more than willing to pay higher prices for organically grown food. But are organic strawberries worth the extra dollar?

The health benefits of organic foods are one of the most debated issues in the food industry. By definition, organically grown foods are produced without most conventional pesticides, fertilizers made with synthetic ingredients or sewage sludge. Livestock isn't given antibiotics or growth hormones. And organic farmers emphasize renewable resources and conservation of soil and water.

The U.S. Department of Agriculture, which runs the National Organic Program, says organic is a "production philosophy" and an organic label does not imply that a product is superior. Moreover, some say there's no need to eat organic to be healthy: Simply choose less processed food and more fruits and vegetables.

The crux of the argument often comes down to the nutritional benefits of organic foods, something that's hard to measure. To compare the nutrient density between organically and conventionally grown grapes, for example, researchers would have to have matched pairs of fields, including using the same soil, the same irrigation system, the same level of nitrogen fertilizer and the same stage of ripeness at harvest, says Charles Benbrook, chief scientist at The Organic Center, a pro-organics research institution.

Last summer, the debate came to a boil after the *American Journal of Clinical Nutrition* published a comprehensive systemic review concluding that organic and conventional food had comparable nutrient levels.

The outraged organic community criticized the study for not addressing pesticide residues, a major reason people choose organic. The study did not address the impact of farming practices on the environment and personal health, either.

Maria Rodale, a third-generation advocate for organic farming, urges consumers to look beyond nutrition to the chemicals going into our soil, food and bodies. "What we do to our environment, we are also doing to ourselves," says Rodale, chairwoman and CEO of Rodale Inc., which publishes health and wellness content. Some experts also suggest that consumers focus on the producers rather than the product itself. For example, Vicki Westerhoff, 54, owner of Genesis Growers in St. Anne, Ill., uses organic procedures but calls her food "natural" and "chemical-free" because she hasn't gone through the expensive certification process.

FRUITS AND VEGETABLES

Farmers using conventional practices treat crops with pesticides that protect them from mold, insects and disease but can leave residues. Organic fruits and vegetables have fewer pesticide residues and lower nitrate levels than do conventional fruits and vegetables, according to a 1996 scientific summary report by the Institute of Food Technologists.

The bottom line: Experts say pesticide residues pose only a small health risk. But fetuses and children are more vulnerable to the effects of the synthetic chemicals, which are toxic to the brain and nervous system, says Dr. Philip Landrigan, director of the Children's Environmental Health Center at the Mount Sinai School of Medicine in Manhattan. The Environmental Working Group recommends buying organically grown peaches, apples, bell peppers, celery, nectarines, strawberries, cherries, kale, lettuce, imported grapes and pears because they are the most heavily sprayed. Onions, avocado, sweet corn and pineapple have some of the lowest levels of pesticides.   As for nutrition, one French study found that, in some cases, organic plant products have more minerals such as iron and magnesium and more antioxidant polyphenols. But although mounting evidence suggests that soil rich in organic matter produces more nutritious food, "we are never going to be able to say organic is always more nutrient dense," says Benbrook of The Organic Center.

DAIRY AND MEAT

Organic dairy and meat products come from animals not treated with antibiotics or genetically engineered bovine growth hormones, which are used to stop the spread of disease and to boost milk production. Past rules on "access to pasture" were vague and didn't require that the animals actually venture into it. But a new regulation requires that animals graze for a minimum of 120 days. In addition, 30 percent of their dietary needs must come from pasture.

The bottom line: The dairy cow's diet is key. Organic milk has more vitamins, antioxidants, omega-3 fatty acids and conjugated linoleic acid because the cows eat high levels of fresh grass, clover pasture and grass clover silage. Research published in the British Journal of Nutrition found that organic milk can improve the quality of breast milk and may protect young children against asthma and eczema.

Though the FDA says milk from cows treated with bovine growth hormone is safe and indistinguishable from other milk, consumers are spooked. Dean Foods, the nation's largest dairy producer, no longer sells milk from those cows, and Wal-mart, Costco, Starbucks, Dannon, Yoplait and other companies have pledged not to use it.

As with dairy, organic meat has higher levels of omega-3's because of the higher forage content in the diet. It also has lower fat overall than meat from animals fed a high-corn diet, says Benbrook. Eating organic dairy or meat also can help with another issue: The use of antibiotics on farms has contributed to an increase in antibiotic-resistant genes in bacteria.

PROCESSED FOODS

Many processed foods — pasta, candy, cookies, crackers, baby food — now come in organic versions. Products made from at least 95 percent organic ingredients can carry the "USDA Organic" seal if the remaining ingredients are approved for use in organic products. Products with at least 70 percent organic ingredients may label those on the ingredient list.

The bottom line: Processed organic food hasn't been shown to be any more nutritious than processed conventional food.

In conventionally processed products such as baby food, pesticides aren't commonly detected because the processing steps "are quite effective in breaking down trace residues of pesticides," says food toxicologist Carl Winter, director of the FoodSafe Program at the University of California at Davis and co-author of the Institute of Food Technologists scientific summary.

"Pesticides are rarely used on crops grown for baby foods since the ultimate appearance of the crop is less important due to the processing before the product is ultimately sold," Winter says.

Cotton and coffee are two of the most pesticide-intensive crops in the world. Pesticide residues have been detected in the cottonseed hull, a secondary crop sold as a food commodity. It's estimated that as much as 65 percent of cotton production ends up in our food chain, whether directly through food or indirectly through the milk or meat of animals, according to a report by the Environmental Justice Foundation. Conventional coffee production also has contributed to the deforestation of the world's rainforests.

The bottom line: Pesticide residues are generally removed during the processing but the chemicals can have a huge impact on the local land, biodiversity and the health of the workers involved. Though buying organic can help preserve environmental health and support farmers who use ecological methods, "it's more important to focus on the circumstances of growers and farms versus the product itself," said food writer Corby Kummer, the author of *The Joy of Coffee.*

ENVIRONMENTAL WORKING GROUP'S DIRTY DOZEN

THE DIRTY DOZEN	12 LEAST CONTAMINATED
• Celery	• Onions
• Peaches	• Avocado
• Strawberries	• Sweet corn (frozen)
• Apples	• Pineapples
• Blueberries (domestic)	• Mango
• Nectarines	• Asparagus
• Sweet bell peppers	• Sweet peas (frozen)
• Spinach	• Kiwi fruit
• Cherries	• Bananas
• Kale/collard greens	• Cabbage
• Potatoes	• Eggplant
• Grapes (imported)	• Cantaloupe

For more information, go to the Environmental Working Group's website at www.EWG.org

Published in *The Oregonian,* April 2, 2010. Julie Deardorff writes about health and fitness for the *Chicago Tribune.*

HEALTH EFFECTS OF MERCURY IN FISH

Compiled by NWEI staff

Coal-fired power plants are the largest source of mercury pollution in the country. When coal is burned to generate electricity, mercury in the coal is released into the atmosphere, and eventually falls to the earth in rain and snow. As the rain and snow enter streams, lakes, oceans and reservoirs, the mercury contaminates many of the fish we eat.

In infants and children, even small amounts of mercury can affect learning ability, language, motor skills and, at elevated levels, cause permanent brain damage. In adults, mercury can damage the nervous, cardiovascular, immune and reproductive systems. Symptoms include tremors, memory loss and fatigue. For more information of selecting safe fish to consume and protecting oceans and marine life, see the following websites:

- Monterey Bay Aquarium Seafood Watch
  www.montereybayaquarium.org/cr/cr_seafoodwatch/sfw_consumers.aspx
- Natural Resources Defense Council's "Mercury in Fish" information card www.nrdc.org/health/effects/mercury/walletcard.pdf
- American Pregnancy Association's listing of highest and lowest levels of mercury in fish:
  www.americanpregnancy.org/pregnancyhealth/fishmercury.htm
- More details on health risks of mercury, especially for young children and pregnant women:
  www.pbs.org/now/science/mercuryinfish.html
- Environmental Working Group Tuna Calculator: www.ewg.org/tunacalulator

Sources: Natural Resource Defense Council, US Environmental Protection Agency
Graphic: Environmental Defense Fund, www.edf.org

PESTICIDE DRIFT

By Rebecca Claren

Teresa Aviña won't open the windows or door of her small apartment, despite a heat that plagues the soul. On the kitchen table, beside two jugs of bottled water, a small, green, electric fan pushes thick air around the room.

"What good is the wind?" she asks, glancing out the window at the breeze that flutters the trees in her front yard. "It's all poison."

When Aviña, sixty-four, first moved to Huron, California,

from Ensenada, Mexico, eleven years ago, the planes that swooped low in the sky, close to the roof sometimes, fascinated her. She'd run outside to watch them fly to the end of her block, where they would drop pesticides like rain onto the cotton fields below.

"I would go outside and look at them without fear. I didn't know I could get sick," says Aviña in Spanish. "Now when I see planes, I run inside and shut the windows. Now I worry about breathing the air. I worry about the kids playing outside."

Todos los días, every day, Aviña says, she smells pesticides. She blames them for her headaches and dizziness, her nausea, for the cancer and miscarriages that have afflicted her neighbors. Like all of Huron's seven thousand residents, she lives near *el campo*, the fields of tomatoes, cotton, lettuce, and melons that ring this cramped town in the heart of California's San Joaquin Valley, the country's most productive agricultural area. In 2006 Huron's Fresno County, one of the valley's eight counties, produced $4.85 billion worth of vegetables, fruit, and cotton. To foster such incredible fertility, growers sprayed nearly 32 million pounds of pesticides using planes, tractors, and irrigation pipe — enough to fill nearly six Olympic swimming pools.

Not all of these pesticides stay on the fields for which they're intended; they may lace the air and drift throughout town onto, say, the playground or Aviña's house. For the most part this isn't illegal. Federal and state law only requires pesticide applicators to ensure chemicals don't drift away from fields during or immediately after application. However, according to the California Air Resources Board, most pesticides volatize (turn from liquid to gas), and become prone to drift, within eight to twenty-four hours after application. Data produced by environmental groups, using statistics and risk assessment methodology from the Environmental Protection Agency, suggests that many of these drifting pesticides float into agricultural towns at unsafe concentrations.

In the past several years, Fresno County growers have applied pesticides an average of 273,000 times per year. The county's Agricultural Commission has twenty-nine staff, each with a host of competing duties, to monitor these operations. Neighboring Tulare County has six people in its pesticide enforcement department to monitor an average of 210,000 applications per year. The California Department of Pesticide Regulation has a toll-free hotline for people to use to report pesticide drift — but it has limited funding to spread the word that such a telephone number exists.

Federal and state agencies have long assured the people who live in these communities that the pesticides pose no threat to their health, that although they may smell chemicals outside their homes, there's no reason to assume they are in danger. But neither the federal Environmental Protection Agency nor state health agencies have launched any widespread epidemiological studies to investigate whether such statements are actually true. The absence of proof isn't proof of absence, and many in the San Joaquin Valley see a willful blindness to potential health problems. And so, for the first time in memory, the Mexicans and Mexican-Americans who inhabit this slice of the valley have stopped waiting for governments to notice them. In an effort to challenge health agencies to better protect them from pesticides, over the past three years a dozen or so individuals in the towns of Huron, Lindsay, and Grayson have taken air samples from their yards. Though they are organized by Pesticide Action Network North America (PANNA), a national environmental group, and supported by regional organizations such as Latino Issues Forum and Lideres Campesinas, it's citizens such as Teresa Aviña — mostly uneducated and poor — who conduct the actual science of air sample collection. ….

Across town from Teresa Aviña's house, on a block that ends where tomato fields begin, live Siboney Cruz, her mother Frances Arguis, and Cruz's five children. Visitors to their home are met by plaster that peels off the exterior wall, billowing pink curtains, and the persistent whine of a generator that powers an odd, capital I-shaped mechanical contraption. Situated just to the right of the front door, beneath an open bedroom window, this two-foot-tall device is a Drift Catcher. While her kids, who range in age from four to eleven, all big brown eyes and shy smiles, play hide and seek, Cruz, twenty-seven, takes a clipboard outside to check the machine.

Powered by the generator, the vacuum cleaner-like mechanism sucks air into two glass tubes, each about the size of a cigarette. Airborne pesticides adhere to an absorbent resin filter that PANNA scientists will analyze at a lab at the University of California, Berkeley. Every day for two weeks, Cruz changes the tubes, noting temperature, wind direction, and any strong smells. Today the wind stirs a nearby cherry tree, and a sharp smell slices the air.

"I get headaches sometimes when I smell this, or I feel sort of frustrated all day," says Cruz. Her round face is pock-marked and scarred, the result of a terrible rash she got several years ago after accidentally being sprayed by pesticides while she worked in the tomato fields. "We go to meetings and public hearings [about pesticide drift], but they don't actually do anything. If [the government] would care about the community, they would do something about it."

The U.S. Environmental Protection Agency hasn't created any federal standards for acceptable airborne pesticide exposure levels for those who live or work near sprayed fields. Dale Kemery, an EPA spokesperson based in Washington DC, explained in an e-mail that "most available monitoring data" suggests that exposure to airborne pesticides is far less of a health concern than drinking or eating these chemicals. He fails to mention that the EPA has only reviewed studies of volatilized fumigants — just five pesticides — to determine whether they may impact neighbors' health. The vast majority of active ingredients in pesticides — nearly a thousand chemicals — have not been similarly assessed. On the EPA website that describes how people may be exposed to pesticides, no mention is made of drift from nearby fields.

State and county government officials also downplay the potential for health impacts. "Everything we do, whether it's cattle with a methane gas problem or pesticides on

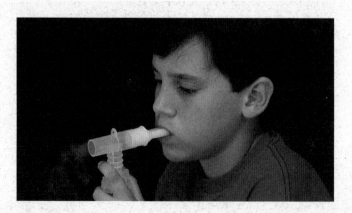

our crops, everything's polluting something," says Karen Francone, deputy agricultural commissioner of Fresno County. "What's our tolerance of it? I'm not here to answer that question. People wearing perfume really bugs me. The person who wears the perfume thinks it smells great. I might say, well, I'll tolerate pesticides because I know it's applied to a commodity so I don't have worms in my fruit. It comes down to what's a person's tolerance." …

In the absence of EPA analysis, PANNA has set out to create its own safety standards. Using EPA data and methodology, Susan Kegley, a former Berkeley professor of chemistry and a PANNA senior scientist, calculated how much of any pesticide a child can inhale without getting sick. The air samples that people have taken over the past several years in both Huron, where cotton and other row crops are grown, and Lindsay, a town ringed by thick groves of orange trees, showed daily evidence of exposure to chlorpyrifos and Naled, both organophosphate pesticides, during the several-week-long sample period. Approximately 28 percent of the time, air samples in Lindsay were above "acceptable" exposure levels for a one-year-old child.

Infant and prenatal exposure to organophosphate pesticides such as chlorpyrifos leads to significant mental and developmental delays, according to recent studies published in *Environmental Health Perspectives* and *Pediatrics*. In one 1998 study, four-to-five-year-old children in Mexico who had been exposed to pesticides suffered significant lags in development — they had more trouble catching a ball, drawing pictures of people, or performing simple tasks involving memory and neuromuscular skills. Other studies link pesticide exposure to autism, infertility, neurological disorders, cancer, and birth defects.

Despite the steady drumbeat of government and industry assurances that such findings are no cause for worry, these reports do concern Drift Catcher operator Siboney Cruz and her mother, Frances Arguis. Most days, the abandoned field behind their house, once a landing strip for crop-dusting planes, becomes a makeshift playground where the kids play tag, duck-duck-goose and hide-and-seek. One of her boys, Adam, nine, has asthma, and when growers spray his wheezing kicks up. In fact, 30 percent of children in Fresno County have asthma, more than double the statewide rate, according to a 2005 survey conducted by the University of California, Los Angeles. "Every time you turn around, an unbelievable environmental justice issue slaps you in the face," says Tracey Brieger, agricultural policy coordinator for Californians for Pesticide Reform, a nonprofit group based in San Francisco. "It feels like the valley is the center of the modern civil rights movement in the country."

According to a 2003 study by Californians for Pesticide Reform, hundreds of thousands of Californians live in places where they're exposed to pesticides that drift away from

farms. Throughout the country, suburban development is consuming agricultural areas, creating communities on the edge of farmland, faster than at any time in history. "Very nice, white, middle-class people will find themselves in this same situation," says Shelley Davis, executive director of the Farmworker Justice Fund, based in Washington DC. "We have this attitude that who cares about them. They're brown and they're poor. But this does not stay in the valley. You can't throw this shit away; it doesn't go away. DDT hasn't been used since 1972 but it persists, it shows up in breast milk of women who weren't even born in 1972. If you don't want this to happen to you, you'd better stop it now."

Luis Medellin lives in Lindsay, another poor community comprised almost entirely of immigrants, about an hour east of Huron in neighboring Tulare County. In the summer of 2006, he and eleven others from Lindsay volunteered to collect their urine every day for two weeks so that PANNA could test for the presence of chlorpyrifos in their bodies. Medellin, twenty-two, works as a dishwasher in a restaurant. He lives in a trailer park surrounded by orange trees, but figured he was young and strong and unlikely to have a toxic chemical in his bloodstream.

Yet Medellin had 7 micrograms of chlorpyrifos per liter of urine, or 4.5 times the amount of the average American adult. He fell within range, just barely, of the EPA's acceptable level for healthy adults (7.9 micrograms/liter). One woman, a former farmworker who no longer works in the fields, had levels twice that. Only two of the study participants worked in the fields during sampling, but eleven of the twelve people tested had levels above the level that EPA data and PANNA analysis indicate would be an acceptable daily exposure for pregnant and nursing women (1.5 micrograms/liter).

"I was mad when I heard about the levels," says Medellin as we walk the orange grove's long, narrow pathways between trees. Mornings after they've been sprayed, he says, the leaves look like they've been sprinkled with flour. "I want to have kids and not have serious health problems. Will this chemical stay in my body and make some damage in the future? Will it stay in my body long enough to cause cancer?"

With a local immigrant advocacy organization called El Quinto Sol de América, and a coalition of regional groups, Medellin and others are working to shield residents from

Thanks to an anonymous donor

pesticides. For the past three years they've pushed for buffer zones between farmland and schools and homes, and for regulations requiring growers to notify schools, hospitals, and residents before they spray nearby. Activists have circulated petitions, held meetings with the Tulare agriculture commissioner and local school boards, and staged protests to attract media attention. They've had some success: beginning in December 2007, growers in Tulare County no longer may apply the most dangerous pesticides by plane within a quarter mile of schools, residential areas, and occupied labor camps. This is the first time a county has used a 2001 state law that permits the creation of buffer zones. Though activists hailed the change, it's far from everything they want. The law only applies to restricted pesticides that require an application permit. Chlorpyrifos, for example, isn't on that list in California.

The accomplishments of the valley residents and the nonprofits that support them may seem minor. But there's a significant, albeit slight, shift in the air. Gary Kunkel, agricultural commissioner for Tulare County, credits the creation of the buffer zones to numerous talks he's had with the activist coalition, and he says that the dynamic between government and local, mostly Latino, communities is changing. "I, for one, ten years ago didn't know the names of all these groups, and now I do. And I think that's a very positive thing. They're becoming increasingly confident and they're getting somewhere," says Kunkel, ruddy and mustached, as he sits at the end of the long, wooden conference table. "They're having an impact and will have an impact on how we do business here."

For this trend, Gustavo Aguirre, a former farmworker from Mexico who is leading the buffer zone campaign for the Center on Race, Poverty & the Environment, credits those like Cruz, Aviña, and Medellin. "It's been successful because of the participation of people in the study. The Drift Catcher and the biomonitoring has a huge impact. One of the reasons the county ag commission can't say they don't like it is because they're not monitoring the pesticides. We're doing their homework for them," says Aguirre. "We are trying to organize rural communities to raise their voices and I think that's happening. I believe people have capacity without limits."

If history is any indicator, the use of Drift Catchers and activism to pull people like Teresa Aviña and Luis Medellin up out of society's margins will take a long time. Even so, the fact that anyone is trying to do something, anything really, not only for themselves but for all San Joaquin Valley residents, carries its own heft.

Published in the July/August 2008 issue of *Orion* magazine. Rebecca Clarren writes about environmental and labor issues for various magazines such as *Fortune* and *High Country News*. She lives in Portland, Oregon.

THE MYTH OF THE BPA-FREE DIET

By Kat Kerlin

Consider a typical cold-weather, American meal: chili. Filled with beans, protein and vitamin-packed peppers and tomatoes, it's pretty healthy, right? Perhaps not when you consider the packaging some of its ingredients come in. If you're like most Americans, you make this meal with a couple of cans of beans, a big can of tomatoes, maybe a can of tomato paste. To wash it down, you crack open a can of beer.

All of those products come in packaging lined with bisphenol A (BPA), a chemical that mimics estrogen and is raising concern among consumers and many scientists for its links to a host of health issues: prostate, breast and testicular cancer; lower sperm counts; obesity; aggression in girls; reproductive and neurological defects; cardiovascular disease and type II diabetes. It's commonly found in everything from canned foods and drinks to hard, clear plastic adult and baby bottles, pacifiers, sippy cups, dental sealants, sales receipts and plastic utensils.

Though reports of its potential health effects and presence in the linings of containers and cans have long been reported in science journals and the media, an article, "Concern over canned foods," in the December issue of *Consumer Reports* has brought concerns over BPA to a broad audience. The magazine's researchers found that nearly all of the 19 name-brand canned foods they tested — soup, juice, tuna, green beans and more — contained BPA, even those labeled "BPA-free." They also found it in some frozen food bags and in packages lined with an epoxy-based material, like some convenience soups in plastic packaging or peel-back lids. The levels varied wildly, with the highest found in canned green beans and soup, and it didn't matter

     Thanks to Mark and Susan Vossler

whether the food was certified organic or not. While federal guidelines for safe levels of BPA are at 50 micrograms per kilogram of body weight, animal studies have shown adverse effects at much lower levels — 2.4 micrograms per kilogram of body weight. One can of green beans accounted for 80 percent of that lower number in a 165-pound adult, according to the report.

It got me thinking, if I were to try to cut BPA from my diet, how might that affect my life? I'd already replaced my trusty #7 (polycarbonate) plastic water bottle with a stainless steel bottle, amid reports that #7 leached BPA. (Nalgene and other companies have since started making BPA-free versions of these bottles.) I knew not to microwave any sort of plastic, as that's been shown to leach a range of chemicals present in various plastics, BPA and hormone-disrupting phthalates among them. But if I stopped eating foods packaged in materials known to house BPA, what would my diet look like?

I decided to find out by challenging myself to a seven-day, BPA-free diet. The parameters: No canned foods or drinks. No food packaged in anything with a waxy liner. (Not that all waxy lined containers have BPA, but some do, and I wasn't sure which ones, so I decided to try to stay away from them all.) Nothing with a metal lid since the coating beneath it has been shown to have BPA, which ruled out almost all glass jars. No frozen foods. And my diet had to be nutritionally sound. If all I ate were eggs and fresh foods, unpackaged in the produce section, I could eat a relatively BPA-free diet (discounting the lining on some of the boxes they were shipped in). But I'm six months pregnant, which was another reason BPA-free sounded appealing, since laboratory animals prenatally exposed to it developed various health and developmental problems, and babies take in more of it per body weight than adults. So I was not going to give up any of the major food groups. …I drew up a careful shopping list, focusing on bulk and fresh foods and headed to the store.

PLASTIC WRAPPED

I decided to visit two stores I knew had a nice bulk foods and produce section. Other grocers in town fit that criteria, but I chose the Great Basin Community Food Cooperative and Whole Foods Market.

By the time I got to the co-op, thoughts of plastic in general were swimming in my head. Though my diet was not to be plastic-free, I wanted to reduce my plastic use as much as I could anyway. Not getting funny looks at the register for sticking all of my produce in a canvas bag without another bag wrapped around them was a nice atmospheric benefit of the co-op. I also got about a pound of dried pinto beans from the bulk section.

At Whole Foods, I found the chicken I would roast on Sunday and then make homemade broth from for Monday night's soup. I found granola for my cereal, wild rice, and nuts

for snacking. I also found myself overwhelmed by how much plastic is used for nearly every food we buy.

The ills of other plastics often accompanied reports I'd read during my BPA research. Polyethylene terephthalate (PET), plastic listed as #1, is linked to cancer, liver and reproductive problems. It's found in soft drinks, salad dressing and ketchup bottles. Polyvinyl chloride (PVC), labeled #3, is linked to autism and cancer and is found in everything from shrink wrap and deli wrap to shower curtains, baby toys and window frames. Looking at aisle after aisle of the grocery store, I found myself both horrified and thankful that my diet challenge was limited only to reducing BPA. Even apples have a little plastic sticker on them, and bulk foods have to go in a bag to get them home. If I were to cut out plastic from my diet completely, I'd starve.

As it was, I ate very well. Breakfast was usually coffee with granola cereal and milk. Lunches were either a cheese and veggie sandwich or baked potato with veggies and cheese. Snacks were fruit, nuts and hardboiled eggs. I'd been soaking the beans since the morning, and they cooked in about two hours. …

There were other items I ate that I was skeptical about: What's the butter packaging lined with, or the salt container or the butcher paper that held my chicken or the olive oil's metal cap? Not being a scientist, I couldn't run any tests, so I took my chances. But it was another reminder that much of what we eat is surrounded in unknown substances. Manufacturers don't have to list "bisphenol A" on the ingredients label.

CHEMICAL ROMANCE

Though too polite to say it directly, Steve Hentges thinks my diet is kind of silly.

"Based on what governments have said, which is based on the science, there's no need for consumers to do what you're attempting to do yourself," he said. "The products you've been looking at — canned food products — what you're doing is avoiding safe, nutritious foods and cost-effective foods at no apparent benefit."

Hentges is a man who still has the first BPA-laden Nalgene water bottle he got more than 10 years ago. He

says he'd even put a #7 container in the microwave and routinely washes plastic dishes in the dishwasher. He's the executive director of the Polycarbonate/BPA Global Group of the American Chemistry Council.

He points to a number of government bodies, including our own U.S. Food and Drug Administration, as well as regulatory bodies in Europe, as having a consensus on the safety of bisphenol A, a $6 billion industry.

Materials from the American Chemistry Council quote the FDA as saying in February, "With regard to BPA generally, based on all available evidence, the consensus of regulatory agencies in the United States, Canada, Europe and Japan is that the current levels of exposure to BPA through food packaging do not pose an immediate health risk to the general population, including infants and young children."

What the American Chemistry Council's materials don't mention is that the FDA's science advisory board rejected that declaration, as it was based on two industry-funded studies, ignoring the hundreds of studies showing adverse effects from BPA. A 2004 review of 115 published studies on BPA showed that 90 percent of government studies found adverse effects at low doses, while no industry-funded study did.

Hentges says the studies the FDA based its decision upon cited more than 200 sources. Nevertheless, after conducting a review of more than 100 new studies on BPA, the FDA was expected to make a new declaration on Nov. 30 regarding whether BPA is safe to use in food and beverage containers, but it missed the deadline. FDA spokesperson Michael Herndon told the RN&R an announcement about the delay was "forthcoming," perhaps within the week. He told the *Milwaukee Journal Sentinel*, "Some things happened that I can't go into that were beyond our control" and that the agency is "pushing hard for some decision soon."

Meanwhile, Hentges says, "I haven't changed anything in my life. I eat canned foods like I always did. I spend my life focusing on the science. Based on what I know, I have no concerns."

CAN'T TAKE THE HEAT

Frederick vom Saal also spends his life focusing on the science, and based on what he knows, he's very concerned. You won't find a single can in his house, and you'll never find him putting plastic in the dishwasher or microwave.

He's a leading researcher on BPA and a biology professor at the University of Missouri at Columbia. He's done several studies on the effects of low-level BPA. His most current research is BPA's effect on "Obstructive Voiding Disorder," a fancy name for when men have trouble urinating. For two-thirds of men who have it, it's related to an enlarged prostate, which can be treated. "If you don't have an enlarged prostate, your urologist doesn't have a clue what to do with you," says vom Saal via telephone. "And if you can't pass urine, it can kill you. With bisphenol A, the question is always, are the outcomes adverse? Well, I consider death a reasonable adverse outcome."

Vom Saal has prenatally exposed mice to BPA and watched as they got older and developed prostate cancer and obstruction to their ability to pee normally. The mice's exposure to BPA was about 10 times *lower* per body weight than what the average adult takes in on a regular basis.

"So we actually can cause one of the most common ailments of aging in men, we can cause that with bisphenol A," says vom Saal.

According to vom Saal, the problem with BPA or any other chemical in food packaging is that we don't know much about them. Food manufacturers don't have to list them on the packaging. The people who make the eight billion pounds of BPA each year aren't required to tell consumers which products they're used in. My confusion over whether BPA was in my butter wrapper wasn't so odd because, says vom Saal, "We have no idea what chemicals are in them because the laws make it impossible for us to find that out. You can never say with certainty yes or no." If the packaging is made from polyethylene (#2, such as milk jugs and plastic bags), they wouldn't be expected to carry BPA, but that doesn't mean they don't.

"One of the things absolutely clear is that most plastics today, according to plastic industry websites, are blends of chemicals," says vom Saal. "The reason plastics are coming out with all kinds of new properties is you take multiple kinds of chemicals and blend them together to create materials with unique strength properties. The idea where you say, 'You don't need to worry, this is made from polyethylene,' well, there's polyethylene, but what are the 30 other things in there? 'Oh, but you can believe it's safe because the FDA says so.' Has the FDA tested it? No. How can we prove them to be harmful if we don't know what they are?"

The FDA is chronically understaffed and underfunded,

as reported regularly during salmonella or e. coli outbreaks. Conflicts of interests between the FDA and various industries have also been established. Dr. David Graham, the "Vioxx Whistleblower" within the FDA's Office of Drug Safety, told Manette Loudon in a 2005 interview, "As currently configured, the FDA is not able to adequately protect the American public. It's more interested in protecting the interests of industry. It views industry as its client, and the client is someone whose interest you represent."

Meanwhile, U.S. chemical regulators use an innocent-until-proven-guilty methodology. Certainty of harm must be established before measures are taken to protect public health.

"It is a perverse situation, where if you're a corporation and you know something bad about a chemical, you're supposed to tell the government," says vom Saal. "But if you don't test it, you can declare it safe. The Europeans just passed the REACH law that reverses that. Now, are we going to be looking like a third-world country in terms of chemical regulation with the Europeans requiring chemical testing but in America, we don't?"

Vom Saal finds the notion of a "safe level" of BPA laughable.

"There is no safe level," he says. "Anything in your body is going to disrupt your endocrine system. How can it be a safe level when estrogen is controlling things in your body and any BPA that gets in there disrupts the normal estrogen your body is producing? If you look at it like, I just want my body to work the way God intended it to and not the way

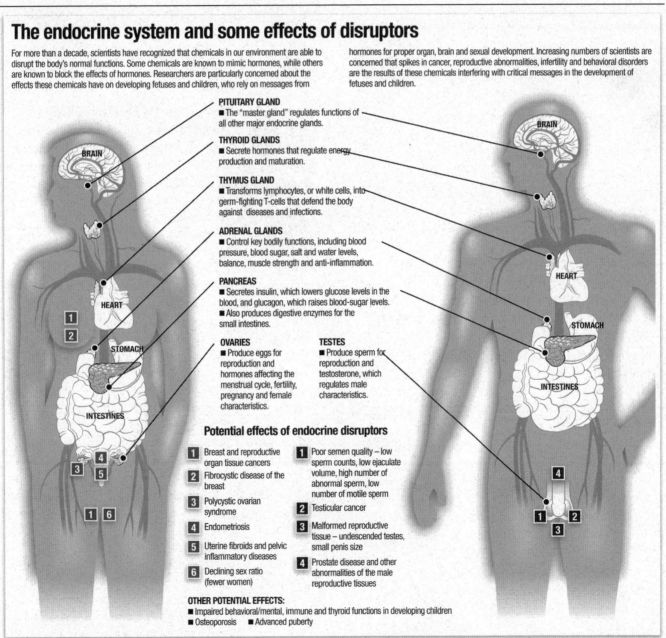

The endocrine system and some effects of disruptors

For more than a decade, scientists have recognized that chemicals in our environment are able to disrupt the body's normal functions. Some chemicals are known to mimic hormones, while others are known to block the effects of hormones. Researchers are particularly concerned about the effects these chemicals have on developing fetuses and children, who rely on messages from hormones for proper organ, brain and sexual development. Increasing numbers of scientists are concerned that spikes in cancer, reproductive abnormalities, infertility and behavioral disorders are the results of these chemicals interfering with critical messages in the development of fetuses and children.

PITUITARY GLAND
- The "master gland" regulates functions of all other major endocrine glands.

THYROID GLANDS
- Secrete hormones that regulate energy production and maturation.

THYMUS GLAND
- Transforms lymphocytes, or white cells, into germ-fighting T-cells that defend the body against diseases and infections.

ADRENAL GLANDS
- Control key bodily functions, including blood pressure, blood sugar, salt and water levels, balance, muscle strength and anti-inflammation.

PANCREAS
- Secretes insulin, which lowers glucose levels in the blood, and glucagon, which raises blood-sugar levels.
- Also produces digestive enzymes for the small intestines.

OVARIES
- Produce eggs for reproduction and hormones affecting the menstrual cycle, fertility, pregnancy and female characteristics.

TESTES
- Produce sperm for reproduction and testosterone, which regulates male characteristics.

Potential effects of endocrine disruptors

1. Breast and reproductive organ tissue cancers
2. Fibrocystic disease of the breast
3. Polycystic ovarian syndrome
4. Endometriosis
5. Uterine fibroids and pelvic inflammatory diseases
6. Declining sex ratio (fewer women)

1. Poor semen quality – low sperm counts, low ejaculate volume, high number of abnormal sperm, low number of motile sperm
2. Testicular cancer
3. Malformed reproductive tissue – undescended testes, small penis size
4. Prostate disease and other abnormalities of the male reproductive tissues

OTHER POTENTIAL EFFECTS:
- Impaired behavioral/mental, immune and thyroid functions in developing children
- Osteoporosis ■ Advanced puberty

Sources: Atlas of Anatomy; European Commission of Endocrine Disruptors; American Medical Association; Mayo Clinic; University of Virginia; colostate.edu; www.innerbody.com

ALFRED ELICIERTO/aelicierto@journalsentinel.com

In memory of C.R. Johnson

the plastics industry says it should work, any amount will disrupt the normal functioning of your system."

THE SEVENTH DAY

My conversation with vom Saal took place on a Friday, and my diet's final day was Saturday. One of the last things he told me was that BPA was in my body whether I was eating from cans or not because it's in the water. Water pipes tend to be made from PVC tubing, and BPA is often used in PVC. It's also in newsprint, pizza boxes, CDs, DVDs, the air. Like he said, we don't yet know exactly where BPA is, but we know that people who've attempted diets like mine still have it in their bodies. Studies have found that at least 93 percent of the population has BPA in their urine.

So by day seven, I admit, I was feeling a little defeated. And my husband wanted a hot dog, so we went and ate a hot dog. And chili was heaped atop the hot dog, and I'm pretty sure that chili came from a can. And I ate it with plastic utensils. And my BPA-free diet was shot.

Yet, today, I don't feel completely powerless. There are ways to reduce the amount of BPA that enters my body. Vom Saal offers a few of them:

- Get an inexpensive carbon filtrating system to attach to your home and work faucet. The carbon can get rid of the BPA before you drink it.

- "Plastics and heat, just stop that," he says. Even if it says BPA-free, the other chemicals in the bottle aren't known, so it's best not to expose it to heat. That means no microwaving plastics — even if they're labeled microwave-safe — or putting them in the dishwasher. "Anything you buy in plastic that tells you you can heat it, assume that is an absolutely insane thing to do," he says.

- When possible, choose glass over plastic or cans. Even if the glass has a metal lid, it's likely to be less BPA than a container fully lined with it.

- If you have to choose between one plastic over another, vom Saal thinks the least worrisome ones are labeled #2 or #5.

Despite regulatory bodies declaring BPA's safety, I think reducing my BPA exposure can only help me and my baby on the way, who will be sipping from BPA-free containers and playing with BPA-free toys, if I can help it. I'll likely make chili from a can occasionally, but maybe less so than before; dried beans aren't that hard to make, especially with a pressure cooker. When I drink beer again someday, it will be from a glass bottle. Canned soup may have to be a rarity. I don't like the taste of canned vegetables, anyway.

EDITOR'S NOTE: In March of 2010, the EPA launched an examination of the environmental impact of BPA. For more information go to www.epa.gov.

Published in the *Reno News & Review*, 12/3/2009. Ms. Kerlin is the Special Projects Editor at *Reno News & Review*.

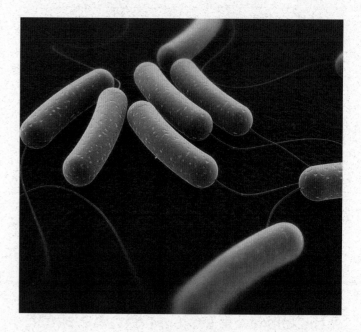

CHEAP EATS

By Ellen Ruppell Shell

Standford economist Peter Timmer is a measured, thoughtful scholar not given to exaggeration, but when it comes to the global markets, one thing worries him above all else. "I'm quite concerned about what the large food companies are doing to the quality and safety of our diet," he said. You need not be an economist to realize that food farmed, harvested, and processed in enormous quantities and sold at very low prices is unlikely to have been handled with great care. Lack of care can lead to sloppiness, and sloppiness to contamination, infestation, and infection. More than two hundred known diseases are transmitted by food through viruses, bacteria, parasites, toxins, metals, and prions, the protein implicated in a number of fatal neurological disorders including mad cow disease and its lethal human version, a new variant of Creutzfeldt-Jakob disease. The less we spend on food, the more likely it is that one or more of these killers will sneak into our food supply.

An estimated 76 million cases of foodborne disease occur each year in the United States, requiring 325,000 hospitalizations and resulting in 5,000 deaths. New surveillance data — and newfound links between food and disease — suggest that these are underestimates. The vast majority of food-related illness goes unreported, and the vast majority of food-related threats are likely to be as yet unknown.

Consider that until the early 1980s few thought that *Escherichia coli* posed a serious problem to human health. The bacterium is ubiquitous and in many ways essential. It resides (among other places) in the human intestine, where it suppresses the growth of harmful bacteria and plays an important role in digestion and vitamin synthesis. Its biological simplicity makes it an excellent model for genetic research, as does its harmlessness. But that is the normal form. Mutated, E. coli can be virulent. E. coli 0157, for example, exudes a powerful toxin that turns on, and attacks, its host. In humans the toxin attacks the intestine, causing severe stomach cramps, high fever, and debilitating bloody diarrhea. In about 4 percent of cases the toxins enter the bloodstream, where the real damage is done. E. coli 0157 infection is linked to the most common cause of acute kidney failure in children, hemolytic uremic syndrome, and also to seizures, strokes, blindness, and brain damage.

E. coli 0157 was first isolated and characterized in 1982, and since then has been linked to what appear to be an increasing number of foodborne disease outbreaks. In 2006 more than two hundred Californians fell ill and three died after eating Dole-brand bagged baby spinach tainted with the bacterium. The bug was traced to the guts of a wild pig caught rooting around a cattle feed lot. One would think three deaths would be enough to motivate the food industry to change its ways, and perhaps in some ways it was. But the following year, in 2007, there were twenty-one beef recalls nationwide for suspected E. coli contamination, the largest number in five years. The amount of beef recalled — 33.4 million pounds — set a new record. A year later, in July 2008, the dangerous strain appeared in hamburger meat packaged and distributed by Nebraska Beef Ltd., purveyor not only to Kroger Supermarkets, but, more surprisingly, to Whole Foods Market, a paragon of the natural foods movement. For reasons no one has fully explained, Whole Foods continued to sell the meat briefly even after the FDA recall. That September the strain appeared in lettuce distributed by Aunt Mid's Produce in Detroit.

Factory farming is efficient, but it is also showing signs of wear. Confined in what might be best compared to a filth-choked slum and stressed beyond reason, livestock are bait for every conceivable pathogen. We can attack them with antibiotics and other drugs, but the microbes are relentless and exact their toll. In 2000 the U.S. Department of Agriculture tracked disease on 895 hog farms, comparing farms with fewer than two thousand animals with those that had more than ten thousand. No one expected the larger farms to be healthier for the animals. Still, it was sobering to learn that when compared with smaller farms, the mega-producers had three times the incidence of mycoplasma pneumonia, six times the cases of swine influenza, and twenty-nine times the cases of a new flu strain. That young pigs tend to die under these circumstances is part of the calculus, mere collateral damage. The survivors live just long enough to stumble over the finish line — and onto our dinner plates.

Livestock doomed to this short, brutish existence exact revenge in subtle but potent ways not only through their flesh, but also through their waste. Traditional farmers fertilize their corn and alfalfa fields with manure from livestock in a closed looped system that benefits both plants and animals. But factory meat growers — the ones with hundreds of thousands of animals crammed into huge concrete floored barns — produce far too much waste to be contained within this system.

It is quicker — and therefore cheaper — to fatten cattle on grain than on grass. Grain feed greatly increases the capacity for E. coli and other microbes to survive in the colon of cattle, where it multiples and gets passed into manure. E. coli can survive up to ninety days in manure, making cattle feedlots fertile breeding ground for infection. As many as one hundred thousand steers at a time fatten on a single lot, pouring out huge volumes of waste. Two feedlots outside Greeley, Colorado, together produce more excrement than the cities of Atlanta, Boston, Denver and St. Louis combined. Trucking the stuff off is impractical. One alternative popular among big companies is to spray liquefied manure into the air and let it fall where it may, coating trees and anything else that happens to be in its path. Another is pumping the mess into lagoons. Both methods have distinct disadvantages.

Lagoons can leak during heavy rainstorms, contaminating wells, rivers, groundwater, and irrigation water. The lagoons also give off fumes of ammonia and hydrogen sulfide, a cause of respiratory and neurological disorders. Manure lagoons also concentrate cadmium, copper, zinc and other heavy metals that can leach into the soil and eventually get sucked back into crops — and into us. And there is the smell to consider. Smithfield Foods, the largest and most profitable pork processor in the world (and among the largest beef and poultry producers), puts out 6 billion pounds of packaged pork a year. A visitor encountering one of the company's manure lagoons described it this way: "I've probably smelled stronger odors in my life, but nothing so insidiously and instantaneously nauseating. It takes my mind a second or two to get through the odor's first coat. The smell at its core has a frightening, uniquely enriched putridity, both deep-sweet and high-sour. I back away from it and walk back to the car but I remain sick — it's a shivery, retchy kind of nausea — for a good five minutes. That's apparently characteristic of industrial pig shit: It keeps making you sick for a good while after you've stopped smelling it."

In July 2007, China blocked imports of U.S. factory-grown pork on grounds of contamination. It is unclear whether these charges were valid or simply payback for U.S. rejection of Chinese processed foods. The United States has reason to be worried about Chinese products. That September, 180 Chinese food factories were shut down after inspectors found industrial chemicals being used in food processing. The closures were part of a nationwide crackdown that also exposed the use of formaldehyde, illegal dyes, and industrial chemicals in the processing of candy, pickles, crackers and seafood. "These are not isolated cases," Han Yi, a director at the General Administration of Quality Supervision, told a reporter. "Han's admission was significant," the report continued, "because the administration has said in the past that safety violations were the work of a few rogue operators, a claim which is likely part of a strategy to protect China's billions of dollars of food exports."

U. S. imports of Chinese agricultural and seafood products have quadrupled in the past decade. From July 2006 to June 2007, the Food and Drug Administration [FDA] rejected 1,901 Chinese shipments; dried apples preserved with a cancer-causing chemical, frozen catfish treated with banned antibiotics, prunes tinted with chemical dyes unsafe for human consumption, mushrooms laced with illegal pesticides, scallops and sardines coated with putrefying bacteria, and the ever popular farm-grown shrimp, this time preserved with nitrofurans, a class of antibiotic that has been linked to cancer. But it wouldn't be fair to imply that the Chinese have cornered the market on tainted food. During the same period, the FDA rejected almost as many shipments from India (1,787) and Mexico (1,560).

Americans claim to put safety first, and one would assume that applies doubly in the case of food. But safety is not free, and we are not always willing to pick up the tab. The United States Department of agriculture (USDA), which is responsible for inspecting meat and poultry, inspects only 16 percent of all imports. The FDA, responsible for fruits, vegetables and most other foods, inspects less than 1 percent of imports, down from 8 percent in 1992. Given this record it takes no leap of imagination to conclude that most tainted imports manage to elude inspection and find their way onto American menus. Blaming exporters for this problem is to shirk our own responsibility. Were we to demand fresher, safer food and be willing to absorb the cost of producing it, tainted imports would be a shrinking rather than a growing threat. The Chinese understand this. Speaking in 2007, Chinese officials begged U.S. importers to communicate standards "more clearly" and "look beyond their emphasis on low prices."

As journalist Paul Roberts wrote in *The End of Food*, "Until late in the twentieth century, the modern food system was celebrated as a monument to humanity's greatest triumph. We were producing more food — more grain, more meat, more fruits and vegetables — than ever before, more cheaply than ever before, and with a degree of variety, safety, quality and convenience that preceding generations would have found bewildering." As prices declined, the sanctity of cheap food was rarely questioned until, over the last couple of decades, it became so cheap as to be dangerous and irresistible.

Excerpt from *Cheap: The High Cost of Discount Culture*, The Penguin Press, 2009. Ellen Ruppel Shell is an American journalist, a correspondent for the *Atlantic Monthly*, and professor of science journalism at Boston University.

THE ONLY WAY TO HAVE A COW

By Bill McKibben

May I say — somewhat defensively — that I haven't cooked red meat in many years? That I haven't visited a McDonald's since college? That if you asked me how I like my steak, I'd say I don't really remember? I'm not a moral abstainer — I'll eat meat when poor people in distant places offer it to me, especially when they're proud to do so and I'd be an ass to say no. But in everyday life, for a series of reasons that began with the dietary scruples of the woman I chose to marry, hamburgers just don't come into play.

I begin this way because I plan to wade into one of the most impassioned fracases now underway on the planet — to meat or not to meat — and I want to establish that I Do Not Have A Cow In This Fight. In recent years vegetarians and vegans have upped their attack on the consumption of animal flesh, pointing out not only that it's disgusting (read Jonathan Safran Foer's new book), but also a major cause of climate change. The numbers range from 18 percent of the world's greenhouse gas emissions to — in one recent study that was quickly discredited — 51 percent. Whatever the exact figure, suffice it to say it's high: there's the carbon that comes from cutting down the forest to start the farm, and from the fertilizer and diesel fuel it takes to grow the corn, there's the truck exhaust from shipping cows hither and yon, and most of all the methane that emanates from the cows themselves (95 percent of it from the front end, not the hind, and these millions of feedlot cows would prefer if you used the word *eructate* in place of *belch*). This news has led to an almost endless series of statistical calculations: going vegan is 50 percent more effective in reducing greenhouse gas emissions than switching to a hybrid car, according to a University of Chicago study; the UN Food and Agriculture Organization finds that a half pound of ground beef has the same effect on climate change as driving an SUV ten miles. It has led to a lot of political statements: the British health secretary last fall called on Englishmen to cut their beef eating by dropping at least a sausage a week from their diets, and Paul McCartney has declared that "the biggest change anyone could make in their own lifestyle to help the environment would be to become vegetarian." It has even led to the marketing of a men's flip-flop called the Stop Global Warming Toepeeka that's made along entirely vegan lines.

Industrial livestock production is essentially indefensible — ethically, ecologically, and otherwise. We now use an enormous percentage of our arable land to grow corn that we feed to cows who stand in feedlots and eructate until they are slaughtered in a variety of gross ways and lodge in our ever-larger abdomens. And the fact that the product of this exercise "tastes good" sounds pretty lame as an excuse. There are technofixes —

In memory of Fritz Bahr

engineering the corn feed so it produces less methane, or giving the cows shots so they eructate less violently. But this type of tailpipe fix only works around the edges, and with the planet warming fast, that's not enough. We should simply stop eating factory-farmed meat, and the effects on climate change would be but one of the many benefits.

Still, even once you've made that commitment, there's a nagging ecological question that's just now being raised. It goes like this: long before humans had figured out the whole cow thing, nature had its own herds of hoofed ungulates. Big herds of big animals — perhaps 60 million bison ranging across North America, and maybe 100 million antelope. That's considerably more than the number of cows now resident in these United States. These were noble creatures, but uncouth — *eructate* hadn't been coined yet. They really did just belch. So why weren't they filling the atmosphere with methane? Why wasn't their manure giving off great quantities of atmosphere-altering gas?

The answer, so far as we can tell, is both interesting and potentially radical in its implications. These old-school ungulates weren't all that different in their plumbing — they were methane factories with legs too. But they used those legs for something. They didn't stand still in feedlots waiting for corn, and they didn't stand still in big western federal allotments overgrazing the same tender grass. They didn't stand still at all. Maybe they would have enjoyed stationary life, but like teenagers in a small town, they were continually moved along by their own version of the police: wolves. And big cats. And eventually Indians. By predators.

As they moved, they kept eating grass and dropping manure. Or, as soil scientists would put it, they grazed the same perennials once or twice a year to "convert aboveground biomass to dung and urine." Then dung beetles buried the results in the soil, nurturing the grass to grow back. These grasslands covered places that don't get much rain — the Southwest and the Plains, Australia, Africa, much of Asia. And all that grass-land sequestered stupendous amounts of carbon and methane from out of the atmosphere — recent preliminary research indicates that methane-loving bacteria in healthy soils will sequester more of the gas in a day than cows supported by the same area will emit in a year.

We're flat out of predators in most parts of the world, and it's hard to imagine, in the short time that we have to deal with climate change, ending the eating of meat and returning the herds of buffalo and packs of wolves to all the necessary spots. It's marginally easier to imagine mimicking those systems with cows. The key technology here is the single-strand electric fence — you move your herd or your flock once or twice a day from one small pasture to the next, forcing them to eat everything that's growing there but moving them along before they graze all the good stuff down to bare ground. Now their manure isn't a problem that fills a cesspool, but a key part of making the system work. Done right, some studies suggest, this method of raising cattle could put much of the atmosphere's oversupply of greenhouse gases back in the soil inside half a century. That means shifting from feedlot farming to rotational grazing is one of the few changes we could make that's on the same scale as the problem of global warming. It won't do away with the need for radically cutting emissions, but it could help get the car exhaust you emitted back in high school out of the atmosphere.

Oh, and grass-fed beef is apparently much better for you — full of Omega 3s, like sardines that moo. Better yet, it's going to be more expensive, because you can't automate the process the same way you can feedlot agriculture. You need the guy to move the fence every afternoon. (That's why about a billion of our fellow humans currently make their livings as herders of one kind or another — some of them use slingshots, or dogs, or shepherd's crooks, or horses instead of electric fence, but the principle is the same.) More expensive, in this case, as in many others, is good; we'd end up eating meat the way most of the world does — as a condiment, a flavor, an ingredient, not an entrée.

I doubt McDonald's will be in favor. I doubt Paul McCartney will be in favor. It doesn't get rid of the essential dilemma of killing something and then putting it in your mouth. But it's possible that the atmosphere would be in favor, and that's worth putting down your fork and thinking about.

Published in the March/April 2010 issue of *Orion*. Bill McKibben is an American environmentalist and writer who frequently writes about climate change and alternative energy and advocates for more localized economies. His most recent work is *EAARTH: Making a Life on a Tough New Planet*, Times Books, 2010.

Watch together or individually before you meet:

JAMIE OLIVER'S TED PRIZE WISH: TEACH EVERY CHILD ABOUT FOOD

A 20-minute video published by *TED: Ideas Worth Spreading*, February, 2010

www.ted.com/talks/lang/eng/jamie_oliver.html

Jamie Oliver is a British chef and media personality known for his food-focused television shows, cookbooks and more recently his role in campaigning against the use of processed foods in national schools, and his effort to improve unhealthy diets and poor cooking habits across the United Kingdom and the United States.

Thanks to Preston and Judy Smith

SESSION 2 — EATING WELL
WHAT YOU CAN DO

If after completing this week's EcoChallenge you are motivated to take further action, consider the suggestions listed below. At your group's final gathering, you will have an opportunity to review the list again and commit to an action item.

Label each of these action items with a code representing its priority in your life.

N: Will do now
S: Will do within the next month
L: Will do within the next year
N/A: Not applicable to me

START WITH YOUR NEXT MEAL:

____ Avoid fast food, junk food, and carbonated soft drinks. Wean yourself and your family from foods that are too sweet, too salty, and too fatty. Experiment and learn to use herbs and spices to flavor foods.

____ Eat organic, local, and seasonal whenever possible

____ Read food labels and avoid processed foods with ingredients your grandmother wouldn't recognize

____ Only eat fish species approved by the Environmental Defense Fund (www.edf.org/page.cfm?tagID=1521), which are low in mercury and not in danger of extinction

____ Other: _____

RESEARCH AND APPLY YOUR KNOWLEDGE:

____ Be mindful of hidden corn in the products you consume, especially high fructose corn syrup

____ Start a compost pile

____ Support your local farms by shopping at farmers' markets or buying a share of a CSA (Community Supported Agriculture) farm. www.localharvest.org/csa

____ Reduce your consumption of canned foods, or start preserving them yourself

____ Eat lower on the food chain: replace meat and fish with legumes (beans, lentils, organic soy) as often as you can, and eat more veggies. Choose pastured over factory-farmed animal products

____ Other: _____

REQUIRES MORE RESOURCES (TIME, ENERGY, MONEY, RESEARCH, PEOPLE):

____ Replace plastic containers likely to leach chemicals into your food with glass or stainless steel

____ Use fewer plastic "baggies" for food storage and preparation. Use less plastic wrap. Use more wax and parchment paper instead of aluminum foil

____ Learn to cook quick and nutritious dishes, and cook for more the one day. Freeze the rest to have homemade fast food readily available

____ Advocate for proper labeling of GMO and irradiated foods

____ Become a co-owner of a locally owned food co-op: www.localharvest.org/food-coops

____ Advocate for removing BPA from canned food linings

____ Grow some of your own organic produce

____ Organize a group to take the Northwest Earth Institute's discussion guide on food, *Menu for the Future*

____ Other: _____

CLEANING HOUSE

*If, having endured much, we have at last asserted our "right to know" and if, knowing,
we have concluded that we are being asked to take senseless and frightening risks, then we should no longer
accept the counsel of those who tell us that we must fill our world with poisonous chemicals;
we should look about and see what other option is open to us.*

— RACHEL CARSON, AUTHOR, *SILENT SPRING*

SESSION GOALS

- To become aware of toxins in and around our living spaces and everyday household items

- To consider ways industry and government can eliminate toxins in consumer products

- To learn ways to reduce our exposure to household toxins

SESSION BACKGROUND

Americans now spend nearly 90 percent of their time indoors, much of that at home. We consider it as a safe haven, a place to escape from the stresses of the outside world. But recent studies suggest they may not be the safe refuges we think — try as we might, we cannot seal ourselves off from "the environment." The readings in this session examine concerns about toxins in our homes, from our cleaning products to our tap water, and offer short and long-term solutions for "cleaning house."

The session begins with an introduction to the "new pollution," as Virginia Sole-Smith describes it in "How to Keep Your Family Safe from Toxic Chemicals." The author gives an overview of the toxic chemicals we are exposed to in our daily life and the health risks associated with this exposure. As an antidote, author Christina Gillham offers a list of "Nine Ways to Avoid Household Toxins."

In "Bridging the Water Divide: It's Not Only About Taste," Carolyn Butler raises concerns about the quality and safety of local tap water and evaluates her options. Going beyond the front door, Beth Huxta examines the impacts of our culture's penchant for green lawns in "The Dark Side of Lawns." In the final reading, an excerpt from *Chasing Molecules*, author Elizabeth Grossman introduces the emerging field of "green chemistry" as a promising solution to removing toxins from our products, our bodies and our planet.

Circle Question

Do you feel overwhelmed or empowered by the information in this session? Explain.

*Circle questions should move quickly — each member responds briefly without questions or comments from others.
Facilitator guidelines are on page 6.*

SUGGESTED DISCUSSION QUESTIONS

1. What was noteworthy or most important to you from the readings in this session?

2. What is the first change that the Healthy Home Assessment inspired you to make?

3. What did you learn from reading the labels of your house cleaners or products you apply to your body? How do you feel about these products now?

4. In terms of your own drinking water supply, do you have any concerns? If you do, what are your options?

5. Should tap water be more strictly regulated? Do we all have a right to clean drinking water? How do we ensure income is not a barrier?

6. How important is a "green" lawn to you? Is there social pressure to "keep up" a lawn in your neighborhood?

7. What would it take to garner more support for green chemistry?

8. Share something you learned from your Healthy Home Assessment and/or Weekly EcoChallenge.

Weekly EcoChallenge: Detoxing Your Home

Detox your home! After completing the Healthy Home assessment on page 48, choose a realistic but challenging way to reduce toxins in your home. For example, replace one personal care product or cleaning item that contains harmful ingredients with a non-toxic one. Take it further and clear it all out! Be sure to check with your local government to find out where and how to dispose of hazardous waste.

To find out more about NWEI's annual EcoChallenge event, visit www.ecochallenge.org.

SUGGESTED READINGS AND RESOURCES

ORGANIZATIONS

Healthy Child Healthy World is a an organization committed to inspiring parents to protect young children from harmful chemicals. Learn more: http://healthychild.org

Environmental Working Group provides a national tapwater database: www.ewg.org/tap-water/home

ARTICLES

Please go to the Northwest Earth Institute website (www.nwei.org) for the most current list of articles relating to this session.

BOOKS

Slow Death by Rubber Duck: How the Toxic Chemistry of Everyday Life Affects Our Health, by Rick Smith (2009). Smith investigates the way in which numerous toxins, present in both our homes and work places, make their way into our bodies, and what can be done about them.

Exposed: The Toxic Chemistry of Everyday Products and What's at Stake for American Power, by Mark Schapiro (2007). Schapiro explores the American government's general unwillingness to do anything to the large companies and corporations primarily responsible for the massive amount of harmful toxins present in many of our everyday products.

FILMS/DOCUMENTARIES

Blue Vinyl chronicles the presence of PVC in numerous products we use every day. It details the many harmful effects the material can have throughout its entire lifecycle, from production to disposal.

"The Story of Cosmetics" by Annie Leonard describes just what really goes into the many cosmetic products we use and the effects they have on both us and the environment. Find out more at www.storyofstuff.com/cosmetics.

As you complete the weekly readings, please remember to fill out the course evaluation on page 7 or go to www.nwei.org/evaluation. Your comments will help NWEI improve the course. Thank you.

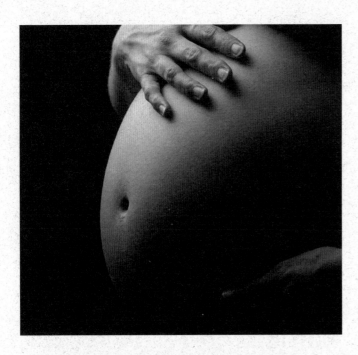

HOW TO KEEP YOUR FAMILY SAFE FROM TOXIC CHEMICALS

By Virginia Sole-Smith

Amy Ellings thought she knew what to expect last year when she agreed to donate blood for a study that would measure the levels of chemicals in her body. It focused on pregnant women in their second trimester in order to gauge what kind of chemical "body burden" they might be passing on to their developing baby. It sounded a little sci-fi, but Ellings, of Olympia, Washington, knew she led a healthy lifestyle: "I'm a public-health nutritionist, so I was interested to see the results, but I figured everything would be normal."

Not quite.

Two months after she gave birth to baby Nick, Ellings learned that her blood samples had contained 12 different chemicals known as endocrine disruptors, which can interfere with the body's ability to produce hormones. Two of these chemicals, bisphenol A (BPA) and diethyl phthalate (DEP), were at levels higher than those found in 90 percent of American adults. "I was blown away," says Ellings. She wondered whether she'd been exposed to these chemicals because she'd grown up in a small industrial town. But BPA and DEP break down quickly, which means her blood test revealed only what her body had accumulated within the previous three days. "I was shocked to learn what my unborn baby and I were exposed to," she says.

You might think Ellings is an isolated case, but biomonitoring studies show that these endocrine-disrupting chemicals (or EDCs) are now found in virtually all of us. The Centers for Disease Control and Prevention (CDC) has identified detectable levels of BPA, for instance, in 93 percent of people tested, and phthalates like DEP in at least 75 percent of the population. "These chemicals weren't in most consumer goods as recently as 40 years ago," says Philip J. Landrigan, M.D., professor of pediatrics at the Mount Sinai School of Medicine, in New York City, and director of its Children's Environmental Health Center. "Now they're in our bodies, and we don't understand all the ways they could impact our health because no previous generation of humans has ever been exposed to them."

What we do know: As the environmental exposures and chemical burden on our bodies has risen, so have rates of diseases, particularly those that impact kids, including asthma, childhood cancers, autism, and ADHD. Hormones, and chemicals that mimic them, may play a key role in the evolution of these health problems because they work as chemical messengers, traveling through the bloodstream to affect the development of tissues and organs, as well as influencing body processes like metabolism and reproduction. "There is no more dangerous time for this toxic exposure to occur than during pregnancy and early childhood, when organ systems are still in development," notes Andrew Weil, M.D., founder and director of the Arizona Center for Integrative Medicine at the University of Arizona.

But nobody knows what level of toxic exposure might trigger a particular disease. Even though many EDCs break down quickly, their levels are constantly increasing in our body because we encounter them every day — in our food, beauty products, and even the furniture in our own home.

THE NEW POLLUTION

EDC exposure works like this: You go shopping and stock up on canned goods, baby formula, cleaning supplies, and shampoo, all of which may either contain BPA, DEP, or other endocrine disruptors or absorb them via their EDC-containing cans and packages. Then you eat, breathe, and in some cases, rub these chemicals directly on your skin. Once they're in your body, you release small doses into our waterways every time you urinate. And when you're finished with the products, you send the leftovers or their containers to break down in a landfill, allowing them to circulate further in the environment.

EDCs do their damage early on, causing small changes to a fetus's developing cells that may have a ripple effect throughout that child's life. "We used to think that the placenta protected a fetus from these kinds of exposures, but studies have shown that phthalates and other endocrine disruptors cross the placenta barrier," says Dr. Landrigan. The Environmental Working Group, a nonprofit advocacy organization, released a biomonitoring report last year that detected more than 200 environmental toxins in the cord blood of newborn babies. Fetuses accumulate these chemicals in higher concentrations than their moms do because their immature liver and kidneys can't excrete them as well as adult organs can. Although Ellings says that 7-month-old Nick is happy and healthy, it's too soon

Thanks to an anonymous donor

suggested links between BPA and increasing asthma rates and cardiovascular problems.

PHTHALATES, pronounced [THA-lāts]

What they are: Chemicals, including diethyl phthalate (DEP), dibutyl phthalate (DBP), and di(2-ethylhexyl) phthalate (DEHP), added to vinyl and other plastics to increase flexibility and to personal-care products to keep their fragrances

Where they are: Anything vinyl; most soaps, lotions, and hair products, especially those with "fragrance" or "parfum" in their ingredients — all of which may off-gas or degrade, releasing phthalate particles into household dust. Phthalates were banned for use in products for kids under 3 by the Consumer Product Safety Improvement Act of 2008, but they're still lurking in many other plastic toys, and any baby products made before the ban.

The risks: "Exposure to phthalates is associated with reduced testosterone levels in kids and adults," notes Tracey Woodruff, Ph.D., director of the Program on Reproductive Health and the Environment at the University of California, San Francisco. Researchers at the University of Rochester have found that prenatal phthalate exposure correlated with subtle signs of feminization (like undescended testicles) in baby boys and less masculine behavior as the boys got older. In April, a study at Mount Sinai's Children's Environmental Health Center also found that children exposed to phthalates in the womb were more likely to exhibit symptoms of ADHD between the ages of 4 and 9.

FLAME RETARDANTS

What they are: Polybrominated diphenyl ethers (PBDEs) are used in products to lower the risk and inhibit the spread of fire.

Where they are: On electronics, furniture, carpets, children's pajamas, and other household items that are required to meet flame-retardant safety standards. As these materials age, they release PBDEs into household dust, which we then breathe in. The CDC estimates that 97 percent of Americans have detectable levels of PBDEs in their body. PBDEs are now banned in several states, so manufacturers will be phasing them out of consumer goods over the next few years.

The risks: PBDEs don't break down as quickly as most other endocrine disruptors, so they persist in the environment and in the body for years. Women with higher levels of PBDEs may be half as likely to conceive as women with lower levels, according to a recent study from University of California, Berkeley. Children who had higher concentrations of PBDEs in their umbilical-cord blood at birth scored lower on mental and physical development tests between ages 1 and 6, according to research from the Columbia University Center for Children's Environmental Health.

to know whether his early chemical exposures will lead to future problems.

These are three of the most common EDCs and the specific ways you and your family are exposed.

BISPHENOL A (BPA)

Bisphenol A (BPA), pronounced [bis-FEEN-al A]

What it is: An industrial chemical that is used to make some types of epoxy resins (which hold things together) as well as polycarbonate plastic, a hard, shatterproof plastic used in some food-storage containers

Where it is: The linings of metal food containers and drink cans and some aluminum water bottles; any food containers, baby bottles, or other plastics that are labeled #7; CD cases; eyeglasses; dental composites and sealants

The risks: "Since the 1930s we've known that BPA can mimic the effects of estrogen in the body," says Richard Denison, Ph.D., a senior scientist with the Environmental Defense Fund. Studies on lab animals have found that early exposures to BPA can predispose them to develop prostate and breast cancers later in life; it may also lower fertility by impairing normal development of eggs and sperm. Researchers at The University of North Carolina at Chapel Hill reported in March that 2-year-old girls who had been exposed to higher prenatal levels of BPA displayed more aggression and hyperactivity, while other research has

HOW WE GOT THERE

Why are such potentially dangerous chemicals allowed in so many household products in the first place? "You can't put a new car on the market without extensive crash testing first, but there aren't any similar precautions in place for chemicals," explains Rick Smith, executive director of Environmental Defence Canada and coauthor of Slow Death by Rubber Duck. When used as industrial chemicals, EDCs are regulated by the much-maligned Toxic Substances Control Act of 1976, which doesn't require that they be tested or proven safe before being used. Instead, it's up to the Environmental Protection Agency (EPA) to show that a chemical is unsafe — that it poses an "unreasonable risk" — before it can regulate or ban that chemical. "The bar is set so high that the EPA can essentially never meet it, and therefore dangerous chemicals are in all sorts of products," says Dr. Denison. Congress's original rationale for giving a pass to industrial chemicals like BPA, he explains, is that they weren't designed to be biologically active or get into our body in the same way pesticides or drugs would, and wouldn't pose the same risks. "Now we know that was naive. We should presume these chemicals could be a problem until their producers can prove otherwise," he says.

Some canned-goods manufacturers, such as General Mills (which makes Muir Glen Organic Tomatoes) and Heinz, are responding to consumer concerns. They're reformulating some of their products to be BPA-free or are planning to line their cans with safer chemicals (which they haven't yet identified). But public-health officials worry that until better procedures are in place to regulate claims like "BPA-free," consumers can't be assured seeing this term on a label means a product is safe. (Experts predict the next hallmark of safety may be products marketed as "EA-free," for estrogenic activity.) "At this point it's still better to choose items that are BPA-free," says Dr. Woodruff.

Meanwhile, some experts continue to believe that the EDC levels found in biomonitoring studies are too low to be a cause for concern. "It's the amount of any given chemical, not its presence or absence, that determines its potential for harm," says Carl Winter, Ph.D., a toxicologist and director of the FoodSafe Program at the University of California, Davis, as well as the scientific spokesperson for a trade group called the Institute of Food Technologists. Still, consider a 2005 study conducted at Carnegie Mellon University, in Pittsburgh, which found that mice exposed to BPA in utero at a level of just 25 parts per trillion experienced double the amount of milk-duct growth as mice with no BPA exposure. That alone would lead you to believe that even the tiniest amount could affect your body.

"Finding any synthetic chemical in a person's body should be a big red flag that we need to really study that chemical," says Gina Solomon, M.D., a senior scientist at the Natural Resources Defense Council. The American Medical Association issued a statement last fall calling for the government to increase regulation of EDCs in consumer products. And certain EDCs are banned in multiple states and cities, including Connecticut, Maryland, Michigan, Washington, and Wisconsin, Chicago, and New York's Suffolk County. Suffolk County, for instance, issues a $500 fine to stores that sell baby bottles or sippy cups that are made with BPA.

In April, Senator Frank Lautenberg (D-NJ) and Congressman Henry Waxman (D-CA) introduced Senate and House versions of the Safe Chemicals Act of 2010, which would overhaul the Toxic Substances Control Act. Under this new law, manufacturers would have to demonstrate that new chemicals are safe before they can put them on the market, and all existing chemicals would have to be assessed for safety over the next five to 15 years. The Obama administration has signaled that it will support the bill. And in April, a panel that advises the president on cancer issued a 200-plus-page report calling for all levels of government "to protect every American from needless disease through rigorous regulation of environmental pollutants," including BPA. "We expect the chemical industry to fight reform tooth and nail, but there's broad bipartisan support for more regulation because nobody in his right mind supports exposing kids to toxins," says Smith.

MAKING A DIFFERENCE

With EDC exposure so ubiquitous, you may wonder if you can keep your family safe. "The good news is that it's completely doable to make small changes that have real benefits," says Dr. Woodruff. For example, many of these chemicals pile up in household dust, so dusting, wet mopping, and vacuuming frequently can reduce your family's exposure, especially if your child is crawling and at that stage where he's putting everything in his mouth. (See "Safer Swaps," below, for more simple substitutions.) "Since many of the EDCs have a short half-life, they can be quickly flushed out of your body once the exposure is removed," explains Smith. Which is exactly what we want to hear as we wait for chemical-policy reform and for scientists to understand the full scope of these daily yet preventable EDC exposures. As Amy Ellings says, "You shouldn't have to worry every time you shop for your family."

Safer Swaps: Whether you make one, some, or all, your family's health will benefit — and fast.

PHTHALATES

Instead of: Personal-care products that list "fragrance" as an ingredient.

Try: Fragrance-free shampoo, moisturizer, and other staples. Find safer products by checking their ratings in the Environmental Working Group's Skin Deep Cosmetic Safety Database at cosmeticsdatabase.com.

Instead of: Heavily fragranced cleaning products

Try: A spray bottle filled with a solution of half vinegar, half water.

Instead of: Buying new toys without knowing what they may contain.

Try: Seeing whether their test results are listed on healthystuff.org, an online database of more than 5,000 products run by the Ecology Center, a Michigan environmental nonprofit.

BPA

Instead of: A water bottle that's made of plastic or aluminum (which may be lined with BPA)

Try: Stainless steel

Instead of: Canned goods

Try: Soups or tomatoes that are packaged in glass jars; fresh or frozen produce; dried beans

Instead of: Liquid formula in metal cans

Try: Powdered formula in cardboard or plastic. If you must use liquid, choose concentrate in glass or plastic.

Instead of: Microwaving in plastic or pouring hot liquids into BPA-containing bottles or containers

Try: Transferring your leftovers to a glass or ceramic bowl before you heat them up, heating baby formula in BPA-free bottles or by putting the bottle in a bowl of warm water.

Instead of: Using any plastic, especially baby bottles and other children's products, labeled #7 (polycarbonate) or #3 (PVC)

Try: Remembering this mantra: "4, 5, 1, and 2 — all the rest are bad for you." Look for a product labeled BPA-free and find out why it's safer.. Lifewithoutplastic.com has more ideas for affordable, nonplastic food-storage containers, bottles, and children's goods. When you do use plastic of any kind, don't put it in the dishwasher.

PBDES

Instead of: Carpets, curtains, and furniture that have been treated with flame retardants

Try: Naturally fire-resistant wool, hemp, and cotton. (With furniture, and other big purchases, before you buy always ask the manufacturer whether it uses a chemical coating.)

TAKE ACTION FOR TOUGHER CHEMICAL LAWS

Check out these Web resources to get involved.

Through the Environmental Defense Fund, send a letter to your Congressperson, letting him or her know that tougher chemical regulation is important to you: edf.org/chemicalsafety.

Stay up-to-date on pending legislation with the Safer Chemicals, Healthy Families coalition: saferchemicals.org.

Learn more about the research of the Washington Toxics Coalition, which conducted Amy Ellings's test: watoxics.org/publications/earliestexposures.

Originally published in the August 2010 issue of *Parents* magazine. Virginia Sole-Smith is a freelance journalist in New York. She was Associate Health Editor at *Organic Style Magazine*.

NINE WAYS TO AVOID HOUSEHOLD TOXINS

By Christina Gillham

Nena Baker, author of *The Body Toxic*, offers her tips for reducing your exposure to everyday toxins.

1. Filter Your Water. A simple water filter can capture a lot of pollutants. Some cities' water supplies can contain trace amounts of arsenic, lead, perchlorate and/or atrazine, a pesticide that may cause cardiovascular and reproductive problems, and possibly cancer. (Though the Environmental Protection Agency has concluded that atrazine is not likely to cause cancer in humans, it is awaiting the results of further studies.) Traces of atrazine in drinking water are most likely to be found in areas of heavy agricultural production like the Midwest and Southeast. (To find out how safe your city's water is, get a copy of your local water-utility report at the EPA's water-safety site www.epa.gov/safewater/dwinfo/ or go to www.nytimes.com/water-data.)

2. Know What's in Your Grooming Products. Shampoos, lotions and makeup can contain a number of toxins like **parabens** and **phthalates**, which have been identified as hormone disruptors and may be linked to certain cancers. When shopping for cosmetics and personal-care products, read the ingredients labels — avoid anything that includes the words "paraben" (often used as a suffix, as in methylparaben) or "phthalate" (listed as dibutyl and diethylhexyl or just "fragrance"). If there isn't an ingredients list, log on to cosmeticsdatabase.com, a source devised by the Environmental Working Group (ewg.org) that identifies the toxic ingredients of thousands of personal-care products.

3. Don't Eat Microwave Popcorn. The inside of a microwave popcorn bag is usually coated with a perfluorinated chemical (PFC) called a fluorotelomer that can break down to form perfluorooctanoic acid (PFOA). Designed to prevent oil from seeping through the bag, PFOA can migrate into the food when heated. It has been linked to cancer and birth defects in animals and preliminary epidemiological studies suggest that a pregnant woman's exposure to PFOA may reduce her baby's birth weight. Moreover, the EPA's scientific advisory board has recommended that the chemical be listed as a likely human carcinogen. The good news is that the EPA has asked manufacturers to work toward eliminating PFOA from their products by 2015. While it's unknown what level of exposure from popcorn bags is harmful, Baker says that consumers should be aware that any exposure could result in very long lasting presence of the chemical in your body. Some perfluorinated compounds are extremely persistent and never break down in the environment, she explains.

4. Don't Get Stain-Protection Treatment. This is an extra you can add to new furniture, shoes or clothes, but Baker says you should avoid this option because these treatments usually contain perfluorinated chemicals. "If you use this on new furniture, it's going to be in your home; you're going to breathe it," she says. Baker also recommends avoiding pots and pans that have a nonstick coating. While nonstick materials are not made of perfluorinated chemicals, the substance is often used in their production. If the pan gets scratched or worn, the chemicals can be released into the air, says Baker.

5. Limit Use of Canned Food and Plastic Containers. Baker recommends reducing your intake of canned foods. Most canned goods are coated with a resin lining derived from Bisphenol-A (BPA), which recently made headlines because of its presence in the plastic used in some baby bottles. A component of polycarbonate plastic, BPA may be linked to certain cancers, fertility and behavioral problems in children. The risk is especially great when exposure occurs in the womb; women who are pregnant or are thinking of becoming pregnant and young children should be especially careful of their canned-food intake.

Not all plastics contain BPA, but because it can leach into food when heated, Baker suggests that consumers avoid heating foods in plastic containers. "If you can avoid heating plastic, it's probably a good thing to do." She suggests using glass or ceramic containers for heating food instead. BPA can also leach into food when it is scratched or worn; so to be safe, if you have a water bottle or other plastic container, discard it if it becomes scratched or clouded.

6. Use PBDE-Free Electronics. Polybrominated

Diphenyl Ethers (PBDE) are a family of flame retardants; two types of the chemical were once added to furniture, car upholstery and mattresses, but were voluntarily taken off the market by manufacturers after concerns were raised about their toxicity. Another kind of PBDE remains on the market however, and according to Baker, "it is equally as problematic as the one voluntarily removed from the market." The chemical, most commonly found in TVs and computer monitors, is stirred into the equipment's plastic and can heat up over time, causing the material to break away and settle into the dust. Many manufacturers have stopped using PBDEs for electronics, but not all have. Check with the manufacturer to determine if your goods contain PBDE. You can find a list of PBDE-free products at the Environmental Working Group's website: www.ewg.org.

7. Don't Use Paint Made With Volatile Organic Compounds (VOC). VOCs include a variety of chemicals and are found in some household products like paint and paint strippers. They are emitted as gases and have been associated with allergies, breathing problems and asthma, and are suspected to cause cancer, according to the EPA. Fortunately, low-VOC and no-VOC paints are readily available.

8. Patronize a Perc-Free Dry Cleaner. Perchloroethylene (perc) is also a VOC and is most commonly used in dry cleaning. The EPA identifies perc as a known human toxin and "a precursor to ground-level ozone (smog)." It usually enters the body through inhalation and remains stored in fat tissue. While many dry cleaners have begun using alternative cleaning practices (the EPA has ordered a phaseout of perc machines in residential buildings by 2020, and California will eliminate all use of perc by 2020), it's best to ask what chemicals they use. If they use perc, make sure you hang your newly cleaned clothes outside for a day to air out the chemical.

9. Dust and Vacuum Weekly. Baker says that toxins like PBDE can settle into the dust in your house, so to be extra safe, it's best to keep your house clean through regular dusting and vacuuming. This is especially important if you are pregnant, have a young child or have a pet, which can transfer the dust through its movements.

This article originally appeared in *Newsweek* on October 1, 2008. Christina Gillham is a journalist for *Newsweek* in New York City.

BRIDGING THE WATER DIVIDE:
IT'S NOT ONLY ABOUT TASTE

By Carolyn Butler

For months now, my husband and I have been fighting about water.

Drinking water, that is. He thinks it's time to ditch our monthly bottle delivery service, because of both the expense and green guilt over all that plastic.

I concede these points but continue to play my trump card: concerns about the quality of local tap water and any potential impact on our family's health. The horrific headlines about dangerous lead levels in the District's water supply from earlier in the decade are still too fresh in my mind; it also doesn't help that lately, filling a glass from our faucet or drawing a bath smells like we're draining a swimming pool.

We had more or less come to a standstill in the water wars when I received an e-mail from the District's Water and Sewer Authority (WASA) at the end of April, warning people in our neighborhood not to use the tap because of abnormally high amounts of chlorine at a local reservoir.

This type of "chlorine spike" is a concern because the disinfectant can react with organic matter in the water and produce higher levels of some disinfection byproducts that have been associated with an increased risk of cancer and DNA damage, said Nneka Leiba, a health research analyst

at the EWG, a Washington-based environmental advocacy group. The April problem was isolated, however, and resolved within a few hours.

While it is comforting to know that our water is being monitored so closely and that this sort of glitch is almost immediately publicized, there are clearly some reasons to be wary of the tap, on both a national and local level. For example, a recent EWG analysis of nearly 20 million records from 45 states identified 316 pollutants found in the nation's tap water system since 2004. Of these contaminants, 114 are regulated and were found in concentrations above federal guideline level; the rest are currently unregulated. "That means these 202 contaminants" — which include gasoline additives and rocket fuel — "can be present in tap water at any level and it would be fine, because there are no safety standards," Leiba said. …

Since 2000, the city has regularly used chloramine instead of chlorine, specifically to reduce the levels of disinfection byproducts in the water. As for lead leaching in from old pipes, [WASA General Manager George Hawkins] admits that it has not yet been eliminated from all home taps, although it is currently well below the EPA action level for problems. "But any lead is cause for concern," he said. The agency recently stopped replacing water mains that are made of lead in all but a few cases, since research found that such replacements do not reduce the amount of lead coming into a house — and might actually increase it for a time — unless the lead pipe connecting the main to the house is also replaced. For people who can't afford such work, Hawkins recommends a simple water filter — preferably one certified by NSF International — which can significantly reduce the amount of metals and other pollutants in your tap water.

And how about that delightful chlorine odor and taste?

It's actually a preventive health measure — the result of a temporary system-wide switch from chloramine back to the slightly stronger chlorine, intended to prevent bacteria buildup and make sure local water lines are clean. The substitution, which started in February, ends this week.

"We saw an uptick we didn't like and wanted to eliminate the issue before it became a problem — to nip it in the bud," said Watkins, who acknowledges that many people notice the change in smell and flavor. For those who simply can't stomach the District's finest tap vintage, either with or without seasonal additives, Hawkins again suggests using a water filter, along with running your cold water tap for five to 10 minutes and keeping water in an open pitcher in your fridge, to help eliminate the eau de swimming pool.

Given such issues, is it any surprise that bottled water sales skyrocketed in the past decade? But just because it comes in a pretty container and by various estimates costs up to 2,000 times more than tap water, that doesn't mean its quality is higher, say experts. In fact, a recent EWG report found that 10 brands of bottled water contained a range of pollutants, including disinfection byproducts, arsenic, caffeine and pharmaceuticals.

"Testing revealed that some — not all — brands look remarkably like tap water, with the same signature contaminants," according to EWG's Leiba, who said that despite labels touting clear mountain springs, various studies estimate that more than 40 percent of bottled waters are sourced from purified municipal public water. "Unlike municipalities, bottled water manufacturers aren't required to disclose any of this information on their labels or websites — so most of the time you have no idea what you're getting."

Indeed, all water is not monitored equally: bottled water is regulated as a food product by the Food and Drug Administration, while tap water falls under the jurisdiction of the EPA and the Safe Drinking Water Act. "These regulations, while similar, are not identical, and in most cases, tap water is better regulated — it's monitored more carefully, the rules for bacteria and viruses, in particular, are stricter, and the reporting to the public is better," said Peter Gleick, author of *Bottled & Sold: The Story Behind Our Obsession With Bottled Water.*

In the course of researching his book, Gleick found more than 100 instances of bottled water contamination leading to recalls in this country alone, a full third of which were never made public. The toxins included mold, fecal bacteria, glass particles and even crickets. "I'm not arguing that bottled water is worse quality than tap water — I'm arguing that we don't know because we're not looking, and that when we do look hard enough and test, we find problems," said Gleick.

So what's a warring couple to do in the meantime, when it seems like the famed poetic lament "Water, water everywhere, nor any drop to drink" has never been more relevant? The experts go with filters. High-quality carbon filters can get rid of contaminants such as asbestos, lead, mercury and disinfection byproducts, while more-expensive reverse osmosis filters will also remove inorganic pollutants including nitrates and perchlorate. But, said Leiba, "Even simple filters can make a big difference in quality."

That may be just the armistice we need.

Carolyn Butler is a journalist for *The Washington Post.* This article originally appeared in *The Washington Post* on May 18, 2010.

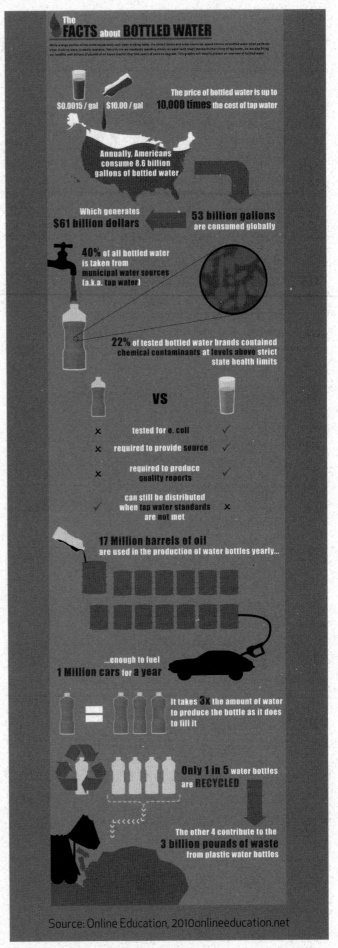

The FACTS about BOTTLED WATER

$0.0015 / gal $10.00 / gal

The price of bottled water is up to **10,000 times** the cost of tap water

Annually, Americans consume 8.6 billion gallons of bottled water

Which generates **$61 billion dollars**

53 billion gallons are consumed globally

40% of all bottled water is taken from municipal water sources (a.k.a. tap water)

22% of tested bottled water brands contained chemical contaminants at levels above strict state health limits

VS

	tap water	bottled water
tested for e. coli	✗	✓
required to provide source	✗	✓
required to produce quality reports	✗	✓
can still be distributed when tap water standards are not met	✓	✗

17 Million barrels of oil are used in the production of water bottles yearly...

...enough to fuel **1 Million cars** for a year

It takes **3x** the amount of water to produce the bottle as it does to fill it

Only **1 in 5** water bottles are **RECYCLED**

The other 4 contribute to the **3 billion pounds of waste** from plastic water bottles

Source: Online Education, 2010onlineeducation.net

THE DARK SIDE OF LAWNS

By Beth Huxta

Americans spend so much money and time on their lawns, you'd think we either eat or sell grass. More land in the United States is planted in turf — 32 million acres — than in corn. The typical American lawn sucks up 10,000 gallons of supplemental water (non-rainwater) annually.

What's worse, the U.S. Environmental Protection Agency estimates that about 80 million U.S. households dump nearly 90 million pounds of herbicides and pesticides on lawns in a year. In fact, lawn care is as much of a danger to our health and the environment as conventional agriculture is.

Does that mean you — and every other organic gardener — must give up having a nice swath of grass where you, the kids, and the dog can frolic carefree? No, not if you follow the plan on page 45. You (and your neighbors) will be surprised to see you can have a thick, lush lawn without toxic treatments.

FOOLS FOR FERTILIZER

The conventional lawn-care industry has sold most homeowners on the need to apply synthetic fertilizer three or four times a season. What's wrong with that?

Nutrient waste. Synthetic fertilizers are chemically processed into concentrated, water-soluble nutrients that are available to plants immediately. But when there is more than the grass can take up, the excess washes out of the grass's root zone and into the watershed. The problem is compounded by the tendency of many homeowners to apply more fertilizer than even the manufacturers recommend.

This nutrient leaching is no small environmental problem. Every summer in the Gulf of Mexico, an area roughly the size of Connecticut is choked with vast algae and phytoplankton blooms, due in part to tons of synthetic nitrogen and

phosphorus fertilizer runoff from the Mississippi River. As the algae dies and decomposes, it uses up the available oxygen, making the area uninhabitable for sea life. The polluted runoff water that contributes to this "dead zone" comes from each of the 31 states between the Rocky and Appalachian mountain ranges that eventually drain into the gulf. This scenario is so widespread that several states, Canadian provinces, and municipalities have imposed bans on fertilizers containing phosphorus.

Weed and feed. The situation gets worse with the widely popular "weed and feed" products that combine a synthetic lawn fertilizer and herbicide in the same bag. "No lawn is 100 percent weeds, but people are spreading these chemicals over the entire lawn," says Paul Tukey, author of The Organic Lawn Care Manual and spokesperson for SafeLawns.org. So if your lawn is 2 percent weeds, 98 percent of the herbicide product applied to the lawn serves no purpose, and it may wash into rivers and streams, leach into groundwater, or volatize into the air we breathe. One of the most common herbicides in weed and feed products, a chemical called 2,4-D, has been linked to human health problems, including an increased risk for non-Hodgkin's lymphoma.

Mystery ingredients. The EPA requires fertilizer and pesticide manufacturers to list only "active" ingredients on a product's label. The manufacturers are not legally required to disclose the inert ingredients, which can include harmful quantities of heavy metals. Inert ingredients in a lawn chemical will not kill your weeds, but there is no guarantee that they will be nontoxic to you or your pets.

PROBLEMS FROM PESTICIDES

Contaminated water. Herbicides and pesticides from lawns also get into our water supply. A study of 12 urban streams in the Seattle metro area found 2,4-D in every stream and 23 different types of pesticides, including five that were present in concentrations high enough to kill aquatic life. The researchers found a correlation between the pesticides polluting the sampled streams and the sales of lawn and garden chemicals from local retailers. And the U.S. Geological Survey's National Water-Quality Assessment Program found that 90 percent of the stream and fish samples surveyed contained at least one pesticide.

Threatened wildlife. Of the 30 most commonly used lawn pesticides, 16 pose serious hazards to birds, 24 are toxic to fish and aquatic organisms, and 11 have adverse effects on bees.

HARMFUL TO HEALTH

Lawn chemicals don't just turn up in the environment. A study of indoor air pollutants found 2,4-D in 63 percent of homes. A different study demonstrated that levels of 2,4-D in indoor air and on indoor surfaces increased after it was applied on lawns.

Not child's play. Lawn chemicals get tracked indoors,

often onto surfaces where kids play. The National Academy of Sciences reports that 50 percent of contact with pesticides occurs within the first five years of life. Such repeated contact has been linked to numerous diseases in children; for instance, researchers reporting in the Journal of the National Cancer Institute found that exposure to garden pesticides can increase the risk of childhood leukemia almost sevenfold.

Women's health. Contact with low levels of pesticides increases miscarriage rates, and a study recently published in the American Journal of Epidemiology documented a link between residential pesticide use and breast cancer risk in women. Researchers at the Harvard School of Public Health found that frequent exposure to pesticides increased the incidence of Parkinson's disease by 70 percent.

Pets smart. Like small children, pets can't read the "Keep Off — Pesticide Application" signs on your lawn or your neighbor's. A study revealed that exposure to lawns treated with herbicides four or more times a year doubled a dog's risk of canine lymphoma, while the Journal of the American Veterinary Medical Association reported that, when exposed to chemically treated lawns, some breeds of dogs were four to seven times more likely to suffer from bladder cancer.

YOUR 6-STEP ORGANIC LAWN PLAN

Growing a healthy, strong, beautiful organic lawn requires not just a change in fertilizers but also a change in mindset. "With an organic lawn, you're not simply putting down fertilizers four times a year; you're initiating cultural practices to nurture life in the soil, and in turn, the soil sustains the grass," Tukey explains.

Transitioning your lawn to organic takes an initial investment of time, effort, and money, because you will need to restore the lawn's soil and the health of the grass. But in the long run, you'll save money and effort as your grass grows healthy and strong and fights off pests and weeds on its own. Whether you've managed your lawn organically for years or are just getting started, follow this step-by-step plan to get the best-looking, healthiest lawn you've ever had.

1. THICKEN YOUR LAWN

Spreading grass seed over an existing lawn is the best way to get a lush green swath that's free of weeds, Tukey says. Where grass is thick and healthy, weed seeds have no place to germinate, and the grass can put down a wider and deeper root system, which can pull nutrients and water from the soil more efficiently. Look for a seed mix specifically labeled for your conditions: sun or partial shade. (Grass doesn't grow well in full shade, so plant other groundcovers in those areas.) And be sure to get a type of grass suited to your climate.

Fall is the best time to overseed, but if your lawn is thin, don't be afraid to do it in spring. Before you start, cut your grass to about 2 inches high to allow sunlight to germinate the new seed, recommends Chip Osborne, creator of the Living Lawn, an organic lawn demonstration site in Marblehead, Massachusetts. Spread about 3 to 4 pounds of seed per 1,000 square feet.

2. FEED WITH COMPOST

Add compost to increase the soil's organic matter content to as much as 7 percent and greatly improve water retention at the same time, Osborne says. To apply compost as a topdressing for areas smaller than 2,000 square feet, use a wheelbarrow and drop small piles intermittently around your lawn; then rake the compost out to about a quarter to three-eighths of an inch, recommends Osborne. For larger areas, use a spreader.

3. WATER WISELY

In summer, lawns account for 40 to 60 percent of residential water usage, but using organic practices — selecting an appropriate grass species for your area, and applying compost — can mean using a lot less water. Water early in the morning to prevent fungal disease and reduce evaporation loss, Osborne advises. Deep, infrequent irrigation forces grass to send roots down into the soil to find moisture and makes it more drought-tolerant. The amount of water to use varies for each grass variety and soil type, but about an inch every week — from rainfall or your hose — is enough to keep an established lawn green.

4. CUT HIGH

Mowing cool-season grass 3 inches high is just as effective as using herbicides to suppress crabgrass, if not more so, according to research from the University of Maryland. Set your mower blade to its highest level. Just be sure to keep it sharp — dull blades leave ragged edges on the grass blades, which allows rapid evaporation of water and makes the grass more susceptible to infection. Mow often, because you never want to cut off more than one-third of the grass blades at a time.

5. LEAVE THE CLIPPINGS

Instead of bagging up grass clippings and sending them to the landfill, invest in a mulching blade for your mower and leave the clippings on your lawn. As they decompose, they add valuable organic matter to the soil and about 2 pounds of nitrogen per 1,000 square feet each season, which means you have to spend less time and money on fertilizing. Contrary to popular belief, letting the clippings decompose on your lawn does not cause a buildup of thatch (a layer on top of the soil that blocks water and nutrients from reaching the grass's roots). Rather, thatch is caused by overfertilizing.

6. FEED RESPONSIBLY

Organic fertilizers come from natural plant, animal, and mineral sources. Once these products are applied to the lawn, soil microorganisms break down the nutrients into a form that plants can take up. Organic fertilizers release nutrients slowly as plants need them, but you still need to follow the directions on the label to avoid overfeeding (yes, you can overdo organic fertilizers, too). In general, apply a low dose in early fall and in midspring.

These steps are simple, and they demand (over time) less work than conventional lawn care. But isn't any effort worth the peace of mind you get from safeguarding your family and the environment?

GO GREEN GUIDE

You can help improve the environment and reduce human exposure to lawn chemicals by raising awareness in your community about the dangers of conventional lawn care and the benefits of organic turf.

Educate your neighbors. Post a "Pesticide-Free Lawn" sign in your yard (find them online at beyond pesticides.org) and talk with your neighbors about the problems with lawn chemicals. Share the simple organic lawn maintenance plan in this article.

Create a demand. Request that your local nursery carry organic fertilizers and lawn products.

Be a positive example. The best way to draw attention to the benefits of an organic lawn is to grow healthy, beautiful grass organically.

Be politically active. Write to local officials to let them know you're concerned about lawn-chemical use in your community and urge them to consider repealing preemption laws, which restrict municipalities from passing local pesticide ordinances that are stricter than state policy.

FACTS AND TIPS

- American homeowners use up to 10 times more pesticides per acre of lawn than farmers use on an acre of crops.
- Reduce H2O flow: Help droughtproof grass by watering it thoroughly but infrequently, so that it develops deep roots.
- Deep roots: A square foot of lawn contains 850 grass plants and 392,000 miles of roots.

INVITING THE OUTDOORS IN
By Deborah Franklin

After enduring one of the wettest winters in Seattle history, Judith Heerwagen, an environmental psychologist and a great believer in the power of nature to restore a weary soul, had to admit last February that 33 straight days of rain had been enough to swamp even her enthusiasm for the great outdoors.

"It got to be pretty grim," Heerwagen recalls. Day after day, her usually splendid window views of trees and a leafy garden were a soupy, storm-battered mess. "Still," she insists, "I'd much rather have a window view of constant rain than no window at all."

And, apparently, so would the rest of us. In the two decades since Harvard University biologist E.O. Wilson first suggested that fascination with nature might be hardwired into the human brain, health researchers and psychologists such as Heerwagen have amassed significant evidence that he was right.

The powerful affinity that Wilson and others have named "biophilia" is more than just puppy love. In hospital studies, Texas A&M University psychologist Roger Ulrich found that surgical patients randomly assigned to a room with a window view of trees not only required less pain medication, but also healed faster and were discharged more quickly than if they had no window or had a view of a brick wall. ….

In ongoing efforts to tease out what it is about some landscapes that makes them particularly appealing, researchers have discovered through cross-cultural studies that certain features — the broad, spreading canopies of clustered trees, colorful flowers or sparkling water, for example — are pleasing to people throughout the world. "People are aesthetically drawn to environmental features that have proven instrumental to human survival," writes Yale University social ecologist Stephen Kellert in his 2005 book *Building for Life: Designing and Understanding the Human-Nature Connection*. Such features, Kellert continues, include "clean flowing water, promontories that foster sight and mobility, areas that offer refuge and shelter, and bright flowering colors that frequently signify the presence of food." The premium price that people are willing to pay for mountain or water views in hotels or homes provide further anecdotal evidence, he says. …

The next step in architecture and other forms of design, Kellert says, is to more fully integrate the principles of biophilia into notions of "sustainable" technology. "I've started thinking of it as 'restorative environmental design' — a concept that incorporates all those principles," he says. "It can't just be about avoiding having negative effects on the environment. We need to think about taking advantage of nature's benefits, too."

Published in the June/July 2006 issue of *National Wildlife Magazine*.

- Home, safe home: Mowing grass high is as effective at controlling weeds as herbicides, which endanger children's health.

- Newbie hint: Control weeds before they germinate, and fertilize your grass with the natural, organic weed and feed: corn-gluten meal. Apply 20 pounds per 1,000 square feet, advises Chip Osborne of livinglawn.org. Put it down in early spring, when forsythia is in bloom, but avoid using corn-gluten meal after overseeding, since it kills grass seeds as well as weed seeds.

- Master's Tip: Apply phosphorus to your lawn only after testing. Even organic sources of phosphorus can seriously affect water quality, and most lawn soils don't need it. Phosphorus-free fertilizers have a middle number of "0".

This article appeared in the April 2008 issue of *Organic Gardening*.

EXCERPT FROM
CHASING MOLECULES: POISONOUS PRODUCTS, HUMAN HEALTH, AND THE PROMISE OF GREEN CHEMISTRY

By Elizabeth Grossman

A few years ago, research into local water quality issues where I live in Portland, Oregon, led me to investigate the environmental and health impacts of the high-technology industry, an investigation that led to publication of *High Tech Trash: Digital Devices, Hidden Toxics, and Human Health*. What I learned fascinated me and prompted wider questions about what scientists are learning about the behavior of many commonly used synthetic chemicals, particularly those that are being released by finished consumer products and making their way into the environment, our food, and our bodies. Why, I wondered, are flame retardants and chemicals used to make nonstick and water-resistant surfaces turning up in seals, sea turtles and salmon as well as in ordinary supermarket food including cheese, chicken, eggs and microwave popcorn? I wanted to know why 95 percent of Americans tested by the Centers for Disease Control had chemicals used to make common

plastics and cosmetics in their blood. Why virtually all the nursing mothers tested in the United States were passing these substances on to their babies. Why people who do not live near, or work in, industrial plants are testing positive for multiple synthetic chemicals, some of which have been off the market for more than thirty years. And why we couldn't design useful synthetic materials without properties that disrupt fundamental biological mechanisms and cause problems that persist, literally, for generations.

There are far more of these synthetic chemicals than could ever be described (here). I've chosen to focus on a number of these that are found in widely used materials, that were introduced for commercial use with the assumption that they were biologically inert, and that scientists now believe can cause serious adverse health and environmental effects. While some of these chemicals have been in use for many years, their environmental and health hazards — particularly their ability to disrupt endocrine hormone functions and other vital biological and genetic mechanisms — have only recently been recognized. Many of these chemicals are found in a vast number of globally distributed products, many of them in everyday use. This has resulted in what are effectively millions of point sources of pollution that are both widely dispersed and in close proximity to people. Altogether, this presents a very different prospect for controlling these hazards than does curbing releases from large stationary sources like factories or waste sites. Although we are also now all exposed to multiple chemicals, scientists have just begun to study the effects of these combined exposures. And although conditions on the factory floor and in farm fields have improved considerably in recent decades, workers worldwide continue to be exposed to hazardous chemicals on the job.

Use of many of the older generation of long-lasting synthetic chemicals Rachel Carson wrote about in *Silent Spring* has been restricted or banned in many places, but these pesticides, along with industrial fluids like PCBs, are actually still with us, as are many other industrial chemicals that have entered the environment over the past four decades or more. These substances are not biodegradable by ordinary processes, and some even resist breakdown through current wastewater treatment, and thus persist in groundwater, oceans, lakes, rivers, soil, ice and snow. Many of these persistent pollutants, both the older and the more recently recognized contaminants, also have a chemistry that enables them to accumulate in fat cells and fat tissue, and thus — as contaminated plants and animals are eaten — to climb the food web. In some locations, warming temperatures are now accelerating the release of contaminants held in place by snowfields, sea ice, permafrost, and frozen soil and as a result are affecting animals — and people — already stressed by climate change.

In memory of Pete Crowell

Historically, regulations and safety standards aimed at protecting human environmental health from chemical hazards have been designed to limit exposure to what's considered an acceptable level of risk — how much of a toxic substance one can be exposed to without it causing observable, measurable harm. In the early 1990s, a new approach to preventing chemical pollution began to be articulated by proponents of what's called "green chemistry," … a discipline that has the potential to transform the world of manufactured materials as well as how we consider a material's safety.

EXAMPLES OF GREEN CHEMISTRY AT WORK

- In 2006, SC Johnson developed Greenlist™, a system that rates the environmental and health effects of the ingredients in its products. SC Johnson is now using Greenlist™ to reformulate many of its products. For example, with the redesign of Saran Wrap® alone, they eliminated the use of nearly 4 million pounds of polyvinylidene chloride (PVDC) annually.

- Adhesives used in manufacturing plywood and other wood composites often contain formaldehyde, which is toxic. Professor Kaichang Li of Oregon State University, Columbia Forest Products, and Hercules Incorporated developed an alternate adhesive made from soy flour. Their environmentally friendly adhesive is stronger than and cost-competitive with conventional adhesives. During 2006, Columbia used the new, soy-based adhesive to replace more than 47 million pounds of conventional formaldehyde-based adhesives.

Resource: www.chempower.org

The fundamental tenet of green chemistry is that preventing a problem — eliminating hazards at the outset or the design stage — is superior to trying to contain or control it once the problem has occurred. Put simply, not sending noxious fumes out of a smokestack is preferable to trying to deal with that pollution once it's in the chimney, let alone drifting through the air. Similarly, if a detergent is formulated without persistent pollutants, we don't have to worry about what happens to the suds after they go down the drain. What successful green chemistry promises is the prevention of chemical pollution by designing materials that are inherently environmentally benign.

An elegantly simple approach, green chemistry actually represents a radical departure from how commercial synthetic chemistry has been practiced. It asks specific questions about synthetic compounds' environmental behavior and toxicity from the beginning of the design stage all the way through manufacture, use and end-of-product-life — questions that typically have not been asked in detail until these materials are launched into commercial production. Answering these questions faithfully and accurately — and with the aim of continually improving product safety — is what gives green chemistry the potential to revolutionize our choice and use of manufactured materials. Green chemistry efforts are underway all around the world, and many successful products designed according to green chemistry principles are now in use. The science is still in its infancy, but the more we learn about the hazards of so many widely used synthetic chemicals, the more compelling green chemistry becomes.

This reading is an excerpt from the Prologue of *Chasing Molecules: Poisonous Products, Human Health and the Promise of Green Chemistry.* Elizabeth Grossman is the author of numerous books detailing the negative effects everyday products can have on human health and the environment, including *High Tech Trash.*

SESSION 3 ACTIVITY: HEALTHY HOME ASSESSMENT

How healthy is your home? The following resources will help to point out ways to eliminate or reduce exposure to toxins in your home. Give yourself 10-15 minutes to conduct your Healthy Home Assessment.

- If you prefer an online "tour," go to www.webmd.com/healthy-home-health-check/default.htm
- If you prefer to use a hard copy, the Environmental Working Group has a Healthy Home checklist PDF you can download at: www.ewg.org/healthy-home-tips/checklist

Consider the following questions to help prioritize actions:

- What area in your home needs attention first? What action can you take to address it?
- What are some simple, inexpensive changes you can make right away?
- What changes require more time and planning?

ROOM BY ROOM, CHEMICALS ABOUND

From the backyard sandbox to refrigerator shelves, endocrine disruptors are widespread in the home

Source:
Milwaukie Journal Sentinel

■ = PROBLEM AREAS AROUND THE HOME

Bathroom

The plastic pipes bringing water into the house are made of polyvinyl chloride. These pipes degrade over time – faster if the water is acidic or alkaline. Phthalates have been shown to enter the body through the skin. Bathing and showering in these chemicals can allow the chemicals to eventually reach the bloodstream. Other offenders include shampoos, soaps, cleaning fluids and shower curtains.

- ■ Put filters on taps.
- ■ Choose fragrance-free cleaning products and cosmetics and try to avoid cosmetics and personal-care products with phthalates and parabens. For details about which products contain these chemicals, go to www.safecosmetics.org.

Kitchen

The food in the refrigerator and pantry is wrapped and stored in plastics that may contain endocrine disruptors such as bisphenol A and phthalates. Bottles for water and juice are often made with these chemicals, too. Countertops are often plastic composites, usually polyvinyl chloride. Plastic wrap, peanut butter jars and salad bags are all potential vehicles for these chemicals.

- ■ Choose plastic food containers labeled with a No. 1, 2 or 5 recycling code on the bottom.
- ■ Opt for glass. For baby bottles and food containers, look for glass options rather than plastics or cans.
- ■ Heat or microwave food and beverages in glass containers or bottles, never in plastic, even plastic containers with No. 1, 2 or 5 labels.
- ■ Buy ceramic, metal or enamel plates and utensils.

Play areas

Most sandboxes, including the Roders', are filled with plastic toys. Anyone who has spent any time around kids knows that these toys, when left outside, begin to fade and crack. That's because UV light breaks down plastic, releasing phthalates and bisphenol A into the air or onto the tiny hands at play.

- ■ Look for "PVC-free" labels on toys.
- ■ Don't let children put plastic toys in their mouths.

Laundry and utility room

Most cleaning and laundering chemicals are packed with **phthalates**. These chemicals are used to hold fragrance, consistency and color in liquids. Dryer sheets are also slathered in phthalates. Detergent containers are also made of plastics that hold other kinds of endocrine disruptors, such as bisphenol A.

- ■ Don't store solvents in your basement or an attached utility room or garage. If you must, open the space to the outdoor air, ventilate, and consider storing hazards in an airtight box.
- ■ Use glues, paints, solvents and fingernail polish outside or in a well-ventilated area.
- ■ Don't use harsh detergents or hot water with plastic baby bottles or containers. Never put them in the dishwasher.

Kids' rooms

The chemicals known to mimic hormones abound from carpets on the floor, to blankets on the beds, to toys in baskets. Many toys, such as dolls or rubber duckies, are made with polyvinyl chloride, or PVC. To make the plastic soft and squeezable, manufacturers add chemicals known as phthalates. These chemicals have a tendency to leach out while toys are being handled or sucked on. The toys become brittle over time – their phthalates infiltrate the air and dust that settles on windowsills and shelves.

- ■ Choose wooden toys.
- ■ Don't let milk sit in plastic baby bottles for long periods.
- ■ Throw away plastic bottles that look scratchy or hazy.

Living room

The carpets, sofas and chair covers in the average living room may be doused in flame retardants – polybrominated diphenyl ethers, or if older, polychlorinated biphenyls – known to have endocrine disrupting behaviors. These chemicals leach into the air and settle into dust. Children who crawl on rugs are especially at risk, because they get enormous amounts of these chemicals on their skin and hands.

- ■ Shop for electronics and furniture that don't contain flame retardant PBDEs.
- ■ Improve indoor air quality by opening windows.
- ■ Avoid tracking pollutants into your home by placing a rug at each entry; remove outdoor shoes there.

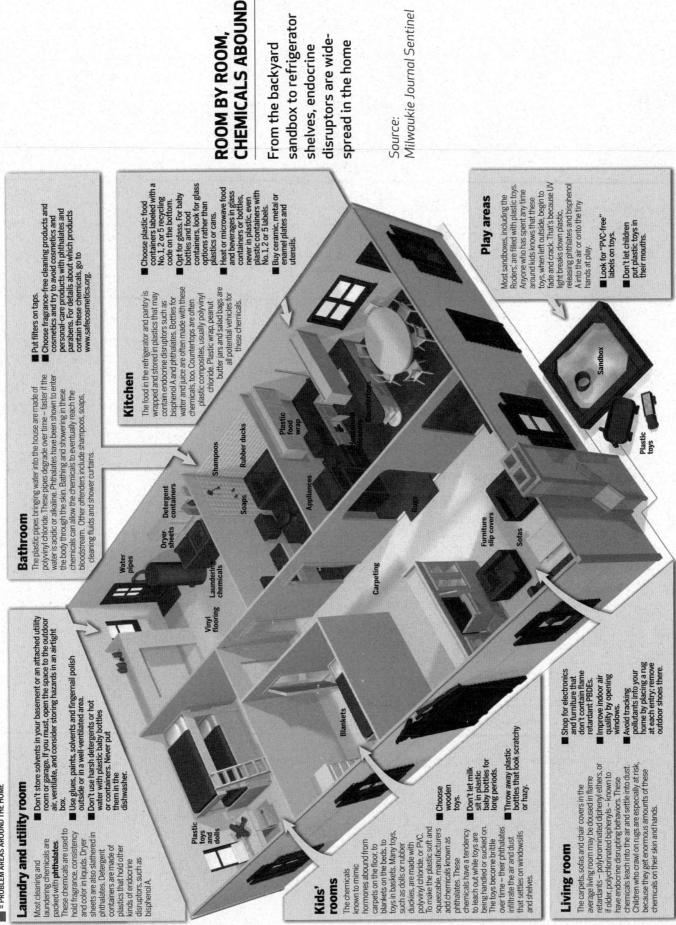

Labels on illustration: Shampoos, Rubber ducks, Plastic food wrap, Soaps, Appliances, Detergent containers, Dryer sheets, Water pipes, Laundering chemicals, Vinyl flooring, Countertops, Rugs, Carpeting, Furniture slip covers, Sofas, Blankets, Plastic toys and dolls, Sandbox, Plastic toys

SESSION 3 — CLEANING HOUSE
WHAT YOU CAN DO

If after completing this week's EcoChallenge you are motivated to take further action, consider the suggestions listed below. At your group's final gathering, you will have an opportunity to review the list again and commit to an action item.

Label each of these action items with a code representing its priority in your life.

N: Will do now
S: Will do within the next month
L: Will do within the next year
N/A: Not applicable to me

BEGIN RIGHT AWAY:

____ Remove your street shoes as soon as you enter your home, to avoid tracking toxic substances inside

____ Open your windows whenever you can, to get rid of indoor pollution

____ Bring plants indoors to improve air quality

____ Never microwave plastics. Cover microwave-safe glass or ceramics with wax paper, parchment paper or white paper towels instead of plastic wrap.

____ Use fewer plastic "baggies" for food preparation and storage.

____ Dust and vacuum weekly

____ Take shorter showers

____ Avoid disposable, plastic water bottles

____ Fertilize cool-season grasses only in the fall (fertilizing them in the spring strengthens the weeds!)

____ Other: _____

RESEARCH AND APPLY YOUR KNOWLEDGE:

____ Make your own non-toxic cleaners: www.ecocycle.org/hazwaste/recipes.cfm

____ Read labels! Know what ingredients to avoid

____ Know what's in your grooming products (shampoos, lotions, makeup): www.ewg.org/cosmeticsdatabase.com

____ Learn more about cell phone safety: www.ewg.org/cellphone-radiation

____ Learn about Integrated Pest Management and organic gardening techniques instead of applying conventional pesticides and herbicides: www.beyondpesticides.org

____ Find a Perchloroethylene-free dry cleaner to patronize

____ Use low VOC (volatile organic compounds) paint and be mindful of emissions from new carpets

____ Other: _____

REQUIRE MORE RESOURCES (TIME, ENERGY, MONEY, PEOPLE):

____ Replace plastic containers likely to leach chemicals into your food with glass or stainless steel

____ Together with other parents, research what your children's toys are made of. Safely dispose of any that contain toxic substances

____ Filter your water

____ Conduct a Healthy Home Assessment and follow through with recommendations

____ Have your garden soil tested yearly, and amend only with what it really needs

____ Conduct a radon test in your basement

____ Advocate for your supermarket to use less plastic packaging

____ Advocate for safe consumer products

____ Other: _____

BUILDING HEALTHY COMMUNITIES

When we see the land as a community to which we belong, we may begin to use it with love and respect.

— Aldo Leopold, American and author, *A Sand Country Almanac*

SESSION GOALS

- To become aware of the environmental health concerns that exist within our own communities

- To examine how community planning and design affect human and ecological health

- To assess transportation options and accessibility in our communities

- To identify ways to reduce driving and increase physical activity

SESSION BACKGROUND

Many of Americans' health problems may be traced not only to what we eat, but also to where we live. The readings in this session examine how issues of proximity to major roads and industry, urban and suburban sprawl, and access to amenities and green space affect our overall well-being. They suggest we can improve public health by designing more "livable" neighborhoods that promote healthier lifestyles and connect us to our surroundings.

The session begins with "Environmental Amnesia" in which Sandra Steingraber notices a "decreasing knowledge about the actual environment itself." Steingraber ponders this lack of awareness and offers explanations for the growing disconnect from the problems outside our own front doors.

Why don't Americans walk anywhere? Stacy Mitchell offers insight into that question in an excerpt from *Big Box Swindle*. Mitchell reveals the negative health impacts of big-box chain stores — on the local communities they open in — and on the planet as a whole. John C. Ryan offers an antidote to car culture with an excerpt from "Why Bicycles are a Sustainable Wonder."

In the final reading, "Leave No Child Inside," Richard Louv reflects on younger generations' growing disconnect from the natural world and the potential consequences for their health and the future of our planet. Louv, who coined the term "nature deficit disorder," contends that we need a "Leave No Child Inside" campaign to reconnect children to the restorative qualities of nature.

Circle Question

Overall, how would you rate your community in terms of promoting health and well-being?

Circle questions should move quickly — each member responds briefly without questions or comments from others. Facilitator guidelines are on page 6.

SUGGESTED DISCUSSION QUESTIONS

1. How much do you know about the history of environmental health in your community? What industries currently operate near you? Do they affect air or water quality where you live?

2. What do you think contributes to a cultural sense of "environmental amnesia?" What are the remedies?

3. What do you see as the positive and negative impacts of having a big box retail store near you?

4. At this point in your life, if you could move somewhere with more public transportation and greater "walkability," would you?

5. How would you react if a big box store made plans to move into your neighborhood? What about a "mom and pop" store or café?

6. Do you feel better when you spend time in "nature?" What differences do you notice?

7. Given the draw of electronic entertainment, can "playing outside" compete? What is a parent to do?

8. Share an insight from the Weekly EcoChallenge or mapping activity.

Weekly EcoChallenge: Driving Less

Get out of your car! After completing the mapping exercise, choose a realistic but challenging way to reduce driving. For example, replace one common driving destination with carpooling, public transportation, walking, or biking. Take it further and plan a car-free day, weekend or week. Take it a step even further by identifying nearby bikeable destinations for groceries, errands, and other outings — then leave the car at home whenever you go there. You could call it shopping *really* local!

To find out more about NWEI's annual EcoChallenge event, visit www.ecochallenge.org.

SUGGESTED READINGS AND RESOURCES

ORGANIZATIONS

Smart Growth America is a coalition of national, state and local organizations working to improve the ways we plan and build the towns, cities and metro areas we call home. www.smartgrowthamerica.gov.

Transition Movement is a vibrant, grassroots international movement that seeks to build community resilience in the face of such challenges as peak oil, climate change and the economic crisis. www.transitonus.org For national centers.go to www.transtionus.org.

Safe Routes to School programs enable community leaders, schools and parents across the United States to improve safety and encourage more children, including children with disabilities, to safely walk and bicycle to school. www. saferoutesinfo.org

ARTICLES

Please go to the Northwest Earth Institute website (www.nwei.org) for the most current list of articles relating to this session.

FILMS/DOCUMENTARIES

The Power of Community: How Cuba Survived Peak Oil (2006) directed by Faith Morgan documents Cuba's emergency transition to local agriculture, renewable energy, and large-scale mass transit.

Play Again unplugs a group of media savvy teens and takes them on their first wilderness adventure, documenting the wonder that comes from time spent in nature and inspiring action for a sustainable future.

"The Story of Bottled Water" details the massive amount of bottled water consumption, when the resource is already available right in our homes, and the great amount of plastic waste this produces. Find out more at www.storyofbottledwater.org.

SESSION 4 ACTIVITY: CREATING AN ACCESSIBILITY MAP

Obtain or create a map of your city or town to assess the success of urban planning, transportation, and other services in the community. Note public transportation routes on the map and whether they run frequently enough to be useful. Consider looking at the location of schools, stores, restaurants, parks, libraries, and other important community resources. Now draw concentric circles a mile radius from your home, 3 miles from your home, and 5 miles from your home.

Consider the following questions:

• Which locations can you walk to? Bike to? Take public transportation to?

• Are there sidewalks or bike paths to amenities in your community? Do you and others feel safe using them?

• What are the barriers to driving less where you live? Are there actions your town or city could take to help overcome these barriers?

ENVIRONMENTAL AMNESIA

by Sandra Steingraber

I would like to report that it takes two hours to jog around the periphery of the Mall of America, the nation's largest indoor shopping center in Bloomington, Minnesota. The two hours includes circumnavigating the mall's 520 stores along with its 20,000 parking spaces, which are mostly contained within orbital rings of monumentally sized parking garages.

I began this run early in the morning and, during my circuit, saw one other human being: a man with a cigarette standing against the largest expanse of brick wall I had ever seen. Near him was a door with no doorknob. From the depths of the parking garages, a few car alarms pulsed, some near, some far, like foghorns. The wind that pours through the loading docks of the Mall of America is fearsome. It slowed my progress considerably.

When I returned to my room in the Ramada Inn — which required crossing fourteen lanes of traffic — it was almost time for my keynote address at the twenty-first annual North American Hazardous Materials Management Conference. I don't believe its organizers intended to make an ironic statement with their choice of venue. They seemed a sincere, overworked lot. They probably figured that the continent's hazardous-materials managers might appreciate the chance to get an early start on holiday shopping.

Ten years ago, I published a book called *Living Downstream* that was about, among other things, hazardous materials. Ever since, I've received invitations to speak about the topic. Wherever I go, I do two things. One, I look up the Toxics Release Inventory for my host-community's zip code. I study the location of the dumps, the routine chemical emissions, the accident reports, the off-site transfers, the permitted releases. And then, once I get there, I run.

Both rituals are ways of paying attention. When I run, I can feel the slope of the land under my feet and figure out how water flows here. I notice the decrepit apple tree that means this subdivision was once an orchard. I notice the aluminum smelter's proximity to the floodplain. Sometimes the names of streets — Creamery Road — provide clues. Sometimes a windbreak of trees does. Even when I'm completely confounded — I cannot tell you how groundwater flows beneath the Mall of America — I discover something amazing. Once, in Livonia, Michigan, while running beside glass office complexes with glabrous names like Techtron and VisTaTech, I veered off toward a small scrim of woods. Within it, three derelict buildings

flanked a derelict tennis court, its green surface shattered by sprouting trees. One of the buildings was entirely filled with chairs. The other was entirely filled with bicycles. Birds flew in and out of slumping holes in the roofs.

During these ten years of running and speaking, I've noticed two opposing trends. The first is that people increasingly believe that their health is affected by hazardous materials in the environment. And they know a lot more about hazardous materials. Pesticides in strawberries. Lead in lipstick. Bisphenol A in water bottles. But there is decreasing knowledge about the actual environment itself. Public awareness is specific to chemicals in consumer products — which are produced elsewhere (increasingly China) and brought into our homes. The location of those homes on former orchards (where arsenical pesticides were used) or near old toxic-dump sites (where drums of solvents were buried) — these matters seem blurrier and blurrier to the folks in my audiences. In fact, I've had to start explaining the word "Superfund," as it doesn't seem to ring any real bells for a lot of people — including people in communities where Superfund sites are present. (Superfund sites are the nation's worst toxic-waste sites. There are 1,305 of them, and they are named for the "super" fund of money put together by Congress in 1980 to clean them up, a trust that went bankrupt five years ago.)

OUR CHEMICAL LEGACY
By Stacy Malkan

Lois Gibbs was living the typical American dream, except that her kids were sick. Since moving to Love Canal, her son had developed asthma and a urinary tract problem and her daughter was diagnosed with a rare blood disease. When Lois learned her son's school was built on a chemical waste dump, she tried to get him transferred but was told that would "set a bad precedent." So she started knocking on doors in her neighborhood with a petition to close down the school. After only a few blocks, it became apparent that the entire neighborhood was sick. Lois heard story after story of cancers, miscarriages and still births. A formal health survey found a high percentage of birth defects in children born in the town. For three years, the families of Love Canal battled the chemical company that denied the problem and various government agencies that defended the company and refused to act, until finally, under pressure from media and the public, President Jimmy Carter signed a bill authorizing funding to permanently relocate the families. Congress later passed the Superfund law to clean up hazardous waste sites. "We stood together and demanded, demanded that the government make right", Lois said. "If a small community of working class families can bring the President of the United States to our stage, we can do anything if we stand together."

Today, while some efforts have been made to reduce emissions and clean up hazardous waste site, most chemicals in commerce are produced using the same outdated, polluting technologies developed decades ago. Every day, the US produces or imports 42 billion pound of chemicals — enough to fill tanker trucks extending from San Francisco to Washington DC and back again. Over the next 25 years, global chemical production is expected to double in size, and the EPA predict 600 new hazardous waste sites to appear each month in the US — adding to the 77,000 hazardous waste site currently in the country. We maybe living longer, but we're living sicker. Chronic diseases and disabilities now affect more than one third of the US population, according to the US Centers for Disease Control and Prevention. Scientific studies have increasingly demonstrated that toxic chemicals are contributing to childhood cancer, hormone-related caners, asthma, learning disabilities, birth defects, infertility and other health problems that have been increasing in recent decades.

Excerpt from *Not Just A Pretty Face: The Ugly Side of the Beauty Industry* by Stacy Malkan, 2007. Stacy Malkan is co-founder of Campaign for Safe Cosmetics and former communications director for Health Care Without Harm.

I was recently invited to Rockford, Illinois, to speak about toxic chemicals. That seemed appropriate because Rockford is the site of a longstanding Superfund site. Solvents used by former businesses had drizzled into drinking water wells. Rockford is famous within toxicology circles because of the bladder-cancer cluster that was discovered here and because it was here where researchers figured out, in the 1980s, that the level of solvents in human blood is predicted not by the amount of water drunk from the tap but by the length of "shower run times." In other words, inhalation is a bigger route of exposure to solvent-contaminated drinking water than drinking it, and showering provides the biggest dose. And yet only two people in my college audience knew about these studies — or even knew that Rockford had a Superfund site. Even the local emergency-room physician hadn't heard the news.

What's inducing this epidemic of environmental amnesia? maybe one contributor is the long silence of the federal government on environmental catastrophes of all kinds. In the breach, activist groups have tried to protect the public. In need of positive messages and deliverable results, they focus on individual solutions. Don't microwave in plastic. Buy organic. There is no place in that discussion for the barrels of waste buried atop the aquifer. The very mention of them fills a room with paralyzing despair.

Or maybe we're now spending so much more time with consumer objects than with our natural environments that we have forgotten how to think about them. Sport water bottles are real to us — polycarbonate? or stainless steel? — but creekbeds are fuzzy concepts.

Or maybe our unremembering is a wall against grief. My own elementary school — along with the field, playground, and wooded path to the crosswalk — was razed years ago to make way for discount shopping. I have steadfastly refused to frequent that part of town. But when my son needed a haircut for my father's funeral, I found myself driving my old walking route to school, in search of a salon open on a Monday. It was supposed to be in here somewhere. While navigating the service roads, I tried hard to forget. But while my son was being pumped up in his pneumatic chair, I saw reflected in the mirror a retaining wall at the edge of the parking lot. *I know that pattern of stones. I looked at them every day during math.* I was standing in my fifth grade classroom. And the military recruiting center next door would have been the lunchroom. And that drive-through over there was the field where, every recess, my sister and Danelle and I ran, circling and whinnying like wild, wild horses.

Published in the May/June 2008 issue of *Orion*. www.orionmagazine.org. Sandra Steingraber is a biologist, author, and cancer survivor who currently makes her home in Ithaca, New York. Her most acclaimed work, *Living Downstream*, details the links between cancer and toxins in the environment.

EXCERPT FROM
BIG-BOX SWINDLE

By Stacy Mitchell

ON THE ROAD

As corporate chains have come to dominate retailing, Americans are logging more road miles each year for shopping and errands. Driving in general has been expanding rapidly, but driving for shopping has been growing more than twice as fast as driving for any other purpose, including commuting to work. Between 1990 and 2001, the number of miles driven by the average household for shopping increased by more than 40 percent. Shopping-related driving for the country as a whole rose by almost 95 billion miles in just eleven years. It's not that we're taking more shopping trips, but rather that more of those trips are by automobile and the journeys are longer. As the chains build ever-bigger stores, each outlet depends on a greater number of households spread over a wider geographic area. Thus, the distance between home and stores continues to grow. By 2001, the average length of a shopping trip had climbed to nearly seven miles, from five miles a decade earlier.

Driving has become less about choice and more about necessity. In much of America, walking or taking public transit to the store is no longer an option. Most families have moved to suburban subdivisions that, by virtue of both zoning codes and convention, are strictly residential and lack the small neighborhood shops common in older communities. Not surprisingly, families that live in the suburbs rely much more on their cars than those who live in more traditional neighborhoods. Researchers at the

University of California recently tracked shopping trips in two San Francisco Bay Area communities, Lafayette and Rockridge, which are similar in many respects. Both are about the same distance from downtown San Francisco. Both have comparable income levels and are served by the same regional freeway and rapid-transit line. They differ significantly in only one regard: Lafayette is a typical postwar suburb with low-density housing served by auto-oriented strip shopping centers, while Rockridge is an older Oakland neighborhood centered on a traditional Main Street lined with dozens of small businesses. This difference has dramatically affected driving rates. The researchers found that, while Lafayette residents make just 2 percent of their shopping tips by a means other than the automobile, residents of Rockridge walk, bike or take public transit for one in five of their shopping trips. Moreover, Lafayette residents travel almost twice as far as those who live in Rockridge.

Corporate chains have a strong preference for locations and store designs that encourage and even necessitate traveling by car. The kinds of landscapes that cars create — vast, homogenous, highly mobile, and divorced from the constraints of place and community — are ideally suited for footloose and fast-growing chains. They, in turn, design their stores in every respect for driving, offering luxurious expanses of parking while creating an environment so hostile to pedestrians that people commonly drive between big-box stores located in the same shopping plaza, rather than traverse the asphalt on foot.

It's not just the design of the buildings and the parking lots but, more fundamentally, the nature of the shopping experience that necessitates driving. Picking up a few things after work every day — which is fast and easy if you have a few good small stores in the neighborhood — is not at all convenient when you have to navigate a superstore the size of several football fields and then wait in line behind families buying a week's worth of supplies. Superstores encourage people to do big shopping trips, stocking up once or twice a week, and that requires having a car to get everything home. This is why efforts to reduce driving by building superstores along light-rail lines or added pathways and other pedestrian amenities to the parking lots are doomed. Even regular walkers and public-transit users are unlikely to visit a big-box store without their cars, because that's what the shopping format demands. University of California researcher Ruth Steiner found that residents of El Cerrito, another Bay Area community, walk to the store one-third as often as those who live in Oakland's Rockridge neighborhood, despite the fact that El Cerrito has nearly the same housing density and plenty of retail within a short distance of residential homes. The essential difference is that, while Rockridge has small stores along a traditional main Street, El Cerrito has a 1960s shopping plaza flanked by a big parking lot and filled with large chain stores. The latter calls for driving and so people drive.

All of these extra miles constitute one of the hidden costs of big-box retail. Part of the price we pay is in lost time: the average adult under the age of sixty-five spends 426 hours each year behind the wheel, including more than 100 hours of driving just for shopping and errands. And they are the fortunate ones: some 80 million Americans are too old, too young, or too poor to drive. As neighborhoods and downtown retailers are displaced by sprawling big-box stores along highways, these nondrivers are having an increasingly difficult time gaining access to basic goods and services.

Driving is also a major financial drain. Transportation expenses account for one in five dollars that the average American household spends. That's more than healthcare and food combined, and double what the previous generation spent, when transportation consumed only 10 percent of the average household budget. Add to these private expenses the additional public costs (not covered by the gas tax) of maintaining roads, and the total bill comes in at close to $2 trillion annually. That's 14 percent of our gross domestic product and almost twice what other developed nations spend on transportation. This counts only direct costs. Indirect costs, such as time wasted in traffic and accident-related costs not covered by insurance, add perhaps another $1 trillion.

But the greatest cost of all is the threat that our dependence on cars poses for the planet and human health. The United States, with only 5 percent of the world's population, consumes 25 percent of the world's oil. Nearly half of this, or 8.7 million barrels a day, is used to fuel passenger vehicles (cars, SUVs and light trucks). Passenger vehicles emit the lion's share of the pollutants (nitrogen oxide and reactive hydrocarbons) that create ground-level ozone or smog. They contribute significantly to acid rain (by emitting nitrogen oxide) and are a major source of carbon dioxide, the primary greenhouse gas causing global warming. As mega-retailers sprawl and driving increases, such activities as buying clothes and picking up groceries

Thanks to an anonymous donor

are becoming ever more polluting. The extra 95 billion road miles that Americans are logging for shopping (over 1990 levels) account for 40 million metric tons of carbon dioxide, 300,000 tons of hydrocarbons, and 150,000 tons of nitrogen oxide released into the atmosphere each year.

The rise of big-box retail has not only spurred more driving and increased air pollution at the national and global level, but it also has created local hotspots of dirty air. As Cleveland has found, big-box power centers and other retail clusters often rank among a region's biggest air polluters. A 220,000-square-foot Wal-Mart supercenter generates, on average, more than ten thousand car trips a day, producing a high concentration of exhaust in the immediate area and annually contributing about 25 tons of nitrogen oxide, 65 tons of volatile organic chemicals (VOCs), 360 tons of carbon monoxide, and 6,500 tons of carbon dioxide to the atmosphere. These localized clouds of carbon monoxide and ozone are hazardous, especially for people with respiratory or heart problems. Sprawling retail — from big-box stores to drive-through pharmacies and fast-food outlets — ranks as one of the worst ways to develop land, from an air-quality stand point. Offices, or light industry, covering the same land area produce only one-eighth to one-fourth the volume of traffic and pollution.

High volumes of car and truck traffic, and the associated noise and pollution, are among the main reasons that no one wants to live near a mega-retailer. The chains have managed to transform businesses that were once neighborhood amenities into nuisances. Consider the difference between a traditional corner store — the kind with a front door that opens onto a sidewalk and an apartment on the floor above — and a corporate convenience store like 7-Eleven. Or between a neighborhood eatery and a typical chain restaurant. The former are mostly welcome neighbors. They offer useful services and social interaction in a format that actually enhances surrounding property values. The latter, with their acres of parking and glowing signs, are noisy, congestive places that reduce the appeal and market value of nearby homes. The unpleasantness of living near most chains has only furthered our dependence on cars. Big-box stores are typically insulated from adjacent subdivisions by large walls and planting, so that even those living next door often have to drive a quarter mile or more to reach the store. Attempts to alter suburban zoning to allow small retail outlets to open within residential neighborhoods are usually meet with fierce resistance, not because people are opposed to a place like Joe's General Store, but because they fear living next door to a 7-Eleven.

◆ ◆ ◆

LONG-HAUL GOODS

The world's big retailers have increased not only the distance traveled by customers, but the distance that goods are transported. One place where this is especially apparent is off the coast of Southern California. Cargo ship traffic jams have become common here since the 1990s as ships arrived from Asia lined up to unload at the twin ports of Los Angeles and Long Beach. Cargo volume at the ports, already among the largest in the world, has been growing by more than 10 percent annually and is expected to triple by 2020. Consumer goods manufactured in China and destined for supply superstore shelves account for most of this flood of new cargo. Wal-Mart is the shipping terminal's top customer. The ports accommodate not only incoming ships, but fleets of outgoing trucks and railcars. All of these engines burn vast quantities of fuel and together make the port complex the single largest source of concentrated air pollution in the region. The ports account for one-quarter of the area's diesel exhaust and emit more nitrogen oxide than Southern California's 350 largest factories and refineries combined. The human toll includes high rates of asthma and respiratory illnesses and a cancer risk twenty times greater than federal clean air standards for those living in neighborhoods adjacent to the ports.

TOXIC PARKING LOTS

While many people recognize the connection between sprawl and air pollution, few are aware that sprawl — or, more precisely, pavement — is now the leading threat to our rivers, lakes and estuaries. After years of steady improvement following passage of the 1973 Clean Water Act, which limited industrial discharges, many water bodies are once again in decline. This time the culprit is polluted runoff from roads, driveways and parking lots. Runoff now ranks as the nation's leading source of water pollution, affecting more than 40 percent of U.S. lakes and streams and leading to fifteen hundred beach closings and advisories since 1998, according to the U.S. Environmental Protection Agency. Every corner of the country has been affected. In Ohio, sprawl is fast becoming the largest contributor of pollution to the Cuyahoga River. In Washington, the once pristine Skykomish River, beloved for fishing and recreation, has seen a startling decline in wild steelhead and salmon numbers. The cause, according to the nonprofit group American Rivers, which in 2005 listed the Skykomish as one of the nation's ten most endangered rivers, is runoff from poorly planned development, especially big-box stores, strip malls, and parking lots. In Vermont, the waters of northern Lake Champlain, which borders the fast-sprawling region around Burlington, have become dangerously dirty, afflicted by toxic algae blooms caused by runoff.

Big-box stores, strip shopping centers, and malls are by far the worst type of development from a water-quality standpoint. No other use of land generates a larger volume of contaminated runoff. This is because of the vast amount of parking these stores require — a two-hundred-thousand-square-foot supercenter typically has a twelve-acre parking lot — and the volume of car and truck traffic they generate, which coats the asphalt with a range of contaminants. "From an environmental standpoint, parking lots rank among the most harmful land uses in any watershed," explained Tom Schueler of the Center for Watershed protection. "Simply put, there is no other kind of surface in a watershed that produces more runoff and deliverers it [to a local water body] faster than a parking lot."

After a field or forest is converted into a big-box store, rainwater that would normally soak into the ground instead washes in torrents across the parking lot and driveways. As it does, it becomes warmer and picks up a nasty stew of toxic pollutants, including phosphorous, nitrogen, road salt, sediments, hydrocarbons from motor oils and fuels, heavy metals, pesticides and herbicides. When this runoff flows into a nearby river, it not only delivers a concentrated load of pollutants, it raises the river's temperature, which harms fish like trout, and changes the watershed's hydrology. Because the ground can no longer act as a sponge — soaking up water during storms and releasing it slowly during dry spells — the river will run very high when it rains, destroying stream-bank vegetation and crucial spawning habitat, and very low at other times, further stressing · plants and fish. Scientists have found that lakes and rivers become impaired when the amount of impervious surface (pavement and rooftops) in a watershed reaches as little as 10 to 15 percent of the total land area. New research also suggests that pavement, which heats up in the sun, is not only contributing to localized "heat islands," but to global climate change.

◆ ◆ ◆

COMMUNITIES VS. LIFESTYLES

Anxiety about sprawl is on the rise, whether it's frustration at the number of hours we spend in our cars, the loss of yet another farm or forest, the dead mall on the edge of town, or the sense that we live, work, and shop in artificially generated landscapes that bear no connection to place or community. ....There are many reasons, then, why we might reconsider our current approach to transportation and land development. There would be substantial benefits to leaving behind the suburban model, where big-box stores and highways reign, and moving toward a traditional settlement pattern — characterized by neighborhoods where the houses are nestled more closely together, cars are not the only means of getting around, and local stores that provide the basics of daily life are close at hand.

Excerpt from *Big-Box Swindle: the True Cost of Mega-Retailers and the Fight for America's Independent Businesses*, 2006© by Stacy Mitchell, Beacon Press. Stacy Mitchell is a senior researcher with the Institute for Local Self-Reliance. She is author of *The Hometown Advantage* and chairs the American Independent Business Alliance.

AT RISK: HIGH-TRAFFIC AREAS TIED TO CHILDREN'S ASTHMA RISK
By Eric Nagourney

Children who live near busy roads are more likely to have symptoms of asthma than those who do not, a study of more than 5,000 children in Southern California has found.

The study, which appears in Environmental Health Perspectives, found that children who lived within 250 feet of major roads had a 50 percent higher risk of having had asthma symptoms in the past year.

The findings, researchers say, suggest that major sources of air pollution like highways should not be the only source of concern.

"At this point, there is enough evidence that there may be a problem with local roads that we ought to think about where we do new construction," said the lead author, Dr. Rob McConnell of the Keck School of Medicine at the University of Southern California.

The researchers found that the asthma risk decreased to normal for children living about 600 feet or more away from a busy road.

The findings were based on a study involving 5- to 7-year-old children in 13 communities. Their families were asked to complete surveys about the children's health. The researchers then charted the answers about asthma against the location of the families' homes.

When it came both to having a history of asthma and to having symptoms currently, the closer a busy roadway, the worse the problem, especially for girls.

The greatest risk was found in children who had lived near busy roads since before age 2, suggesting they might have been exposed to pollutants in infancy or while their mothers were pregnant.

While it is unclear what people who live near roads can do to reduce their risk, Dr. McConnell said some communities had begun passing laws intended to keep new schools farther from busy roads. Communities should also think about where they place their playgrounds, he said.

Published in *The New York Times*, May 9, 2006.   To look up the air quality rating of your community, go to: www.airnow.gov/

WHY BIKES ARE A SUSTAINABLE WONDER

By John C. Ryan

The gist: Two-wheeling ranks as the most energy-efficient form of travel — and makes you healthier to boot. Let's give it more respect.

The details: The bicycle is the world's most widely used transport vehicle. Worldwide, bicycles outnumber automobiles almost two to one, and their production outpaces cars three to one. Rush-hour traffic in China is dominated by human-powered vehicles (though that's beginning to change). Even in the wealthy cities of Europe and Japan, large shares of the populace get around by bike.

Despite its popularity elsewhere, the bicycle gets little use or respect, except as a plaything, in North America. Of all trips in the United States, less than 1 percent are made by bicycle. Some government agencies have embraced bikes, but they remain the exception.

The bicycle — the most energy-efficient form of travel ever devised — deserves better. Pound for pound, a person on a bicycle expends less energy than any creature or machine covering the same distance. (A human walking spends about three times as much energy per pound; even a salmon swimming spends about twice as much.)

An amazing invention, the automobile has given twentieth-century humans unprecedented mobility. Yet cars have proliferated to the detriment of all other means of getting around and at great expense to human and natural communities.

But today, cars so dominate transportation systems and communities in North America that their own usefulness is on the wane: they are crowding themselves to a standstill.

MAKING CYCLING AND ALTERNATIVE TRANSPORTATION A PRIORITY

Activists, engineers, and planners are working hard to promote alternatives to our problematic, car-dominated system. Buses, trains, and carpools produce less pollution and traffic than solo driving, but lack the privacy and door-to-door convenience of cars.

Vehicles powered by alternative fuels or electricity, and proposed "hypercars" able to cross the continent on a tank of gas, could minimize cars' greenhouse gas emissions. But such cars do nothing about the problems of traffic, sprawl, or deadly accidents.

Though a variety of choices is key to reforming our car-centered transportation system, the only vehicle that addresses all the environmental liabilities of cars is the bicycle.

While advertising sells cars and trucks as tools for the open road, they most often help us inhabit a small daily realm — "Errandsville" — defined by home, store, job, and school.

Many of these trips are easily bikable — or walkable — even on roads designed without bicycles or pedestrians in mind. A bicyclist can easily cover a mile in four minutes, a pedestrian in 15.

Short car trips are, naturally, the easiest to replace with a bike (or even walking) trip. Mile for mile, they are also the most polluting.

PROMOTING ACTIVE LIFESTYLES

Increased use of bicycles as transportation could also help reduce the huge toll of sedentary lifestyles on North Americans. In the United States, more people are at risk of heart disease — the nation's leading killer — due to physical inactivity than any other factor, including smoking and fat-laden diets. Forty percent of all American adults get almost no exercise; only 1 out of 13 gets the recommended amount.

Policies from local zoning laws to federal highway funding and tax codes favor driving over all other modes of transport; revised policies can just as effectively do the reverse. Bike-friendly policies, from traffic calming to car-free downtown zones, have boosted cycling rates in five European nations to 10 percent or more of urban trips.

Conditions for bicyclists can be improved cheaply and quickly. Nearly half the recreational riders in the United States — or one out of five of all adults — say they would sometimes bike to work if better bike lanes or paths existed.

Among major U.S. cities, those with extensive bicycle lanes have three times the rate of bike commuting as other cities.

Other nations have already made bicycling a priority: the Netherlands, for example, spends 10 percent of its roads budget to support bicycle facilities.

British author H. G. Wells may have summed it up best more than a half century ago: "When I see an adult on a bicycle, I do not despair for the future of the human race."

Adapted from *Seven Wonders*, which was re-released in 2008 as a climate-change handbook by Sightline Institute, a nonprofit thank-tank committed to making the Northwest a global model for security. www.sightline.org. John C. Ryan is the executive director of Sightline.

LEAVE NO CHILD INSIDE

By Richard Louv

As a boy, I pulled out dozens — perhaps hundreds — of survey stakes in a vain effort to slow the bulldozers that were taking out my woods to make way for a new subdivision. Had I known then what I've since learned from a developer, that I should have simply moved the stakes around to be more effective, I would surely have done that too. So you might imagine my dubiousness when, a few weeks after the publication of my 2005 book, *Last Child in the Woods*, I received an e-mail from Derek Thomas, who introduced himself as vice-chairman and chief investment officer of Newland Communities, one of the nation's largest privately owned residential development companies. "I have been reading your new book," he wrote, "and am profoundly disturbed by some of the information you present."

Thomas said he wanted to do something positive. He invited me to an envisioning session in Phoenix to "explore how Newland can improve or redefine our approach to open space preservation and the interaction between our homebuyers and nature." A few weeks later, in a conference room filled with about eighty developers, builders, and real estate marketers, I offered my sermonette. The folks in the crowd were partially responsible for the problem, I suggested, because they destroy natural habitat, design communities in ways that discourage any real contact with nature, and include covenants that virtually criminalize

outdoor play — outlawing tree-climbing, fort-building, even chalk-drawing on sidewalks.

I was ready to make a fast exit when Thomas, a bearded man with an avuncular demeanor, stood up and said, "I want you all to go into small groups and solve the problem: how are we going to build communities in the future that actually connect kids with nature?" The room filled with noise and excitement. By the time the groups reassembled to report the ideas they had generated, I had glimpsed the primal power of connecting children and nature: it can inspire unexpected advocates and lure unlikely allies to enter an entirely new place. Call it the doorway effect. Once through the door, they can revisualize seemingly intractable problems and produce solutions they might otherwise never have imagined.

A half hour after Thomas' challenge, the groups reported their ideas. Among them: leave some land and native habitat in place (that's a good start); employ green design principles; incorporate nature trails and natural waterways; throw out the conventional covenants and restrictions that discourage or prohibit natural play and rewrite the rules to encourage it; allow kids to build forts and tree houses or plant gardens; and create small, on-site nature centers.

"Kids could become guides, using cell phones, along nature trails that lead to schools at the edge of the development," someone suggested. Were the men and women in this room just blowing smoke? Maybe. *Developers exploiting our hunger for nature*, I thought, *just as they market their subdivisions by naming their streets after the trees and streams that they destroy*. But the fact that developers, builders, and real estate marketers would approach Derek Thomas' question with such apparently heartfelt enthusiasm was revealing. The quality of their ideas mattered less than the fact that they had them. While they may not get there themselves, the people in this room were visualizing a very different future. They were undergoing a process of discovery that has proliferated around the country in the past two years, and not only among developers.

For decades, environmental educators, conservationists, and others have worked, often heroically, to bring more children to nature — usually with inadequate support from policymakers. A number of trends, including the recent unexpected national media attention to *Last Child* and "nature-deficit disorder," have now brought the concerns of these veteran advocates before a broader audience. While some may argue that the word "movement" is hyperbole, we do seem to have reached a tipping point. State and regional campaigns, sometimes called Leave No Child Inside, have begun to form in Cincinnati, Cleveland, Chicago, the San Francisco Bay Area, St. Louis, Connecticut, Florida, Colorado, Texas, and elsewhere. A host of related initiatives — among them the simple-living, walkable-cities, nature-education, and land-trust movements — have begun to find common cause, and collective strength, through this issue. The activity has attracted a diverse assortment of people who might otherwise never work together.

In September 2006, the National Conservation Training Center and the Conservation Fund hosted the National Dialogue on Children and Nature in Shepherdstown, West Virginia. The conference drew some 350 people from around the country, representing educators, health-care experts, recreation companies, residential developers, urban planners, conservation agencies, academics, and other groups. Even the Walt Disney Company was represented. Support has also come from religious leaders, liberal and conservative, who understand that all spiritual life begins with a sense of wonder, and that one of the first windows to wonder is the natural world. "Christians should take the lead in reconnecting with nature and disconnecting from machines," writes R. Albert Mohler Jr., president of the Southern Baptist Theological Seminary, the flagship school of the Southern Baptist Convention.

To some extent, the movement is fueled by organizational or economic self-interest. But something deeper is going on here. With its nearly universal appeal, this issue seems to hint at a more atavistic motivation. It may have something to do with what Harvard professor E. O. Wilson calls the biophilia hypothesis, which is that human beings are innately attracted to nature: biologically, we are all still hunters and gatherers, and there is something in us, which we do not fully understand, that needs an occasional immersion in nature. We do know that when people talk about the disconnect between children and nature — if they are old enough to remember a time when outdoor play was the norm — they almost always tell stories about their own childhoods: this tree house or fort, that special woods or ditch or creek or meadow. They recall those "places of initiation," in the words of naturalist Bob Pyle, where they may have first sensed with awe and wonder the largeness of the world seen and unseen. When people share these stories, their cultural, political, and religious walls come tumbling down.

And when that happens, ideas can pour forth — and lead to ever more insightful approaches. It's a short conceptual leap, for example, from the notions generated by Derek Thomas' working group to the creation of a truly sustainable development like the pioneering Village Homes, in Davis, California, where suburban homes are pointed inward toward open green space, vegetable gardens are encouraged, and orchards, not gates or walls, surround the community. And from there, rather than excusing more sprawl with a green patina, developers might even encourage the green redevelopment of portions of strip-mall America into Dutch-style eco-communities, where nature would be an essential strand in the fabric of the urban neighborhood.

In similar ways, the leave-no-child-inside movement could become one of the best ways to challenge other entrenched conceptions — for example, the current, test-centric definition of education reform. Bring unlike-minded people through the doorway to talk about the effect of society's nature-deficit on child development, and pretty soon they'll be asking hard questions: Just why have school districts canceled field trips and recess and environmental education? And why doesn't our school have windows that open and natural light? At a deeper level, when we challenge schools to incorporate place-based learning in the natural world, we will help students realize that school isn't supposed to be a polite form of incarceration, but a portal to the wider world.

All this may be wishful thinking, of course, at least in the short run. But as Martin Luther King Jr. often said, the success of any social movement depends on its ability to show a world where people will want to go. The point is that thinking about children's need for nature helps us begin to paint a picture of that world — which is something that has to be done, because the price of not painting that picture is too high.

Within the space of a few decades, the way children understand and experience their neighborhoods and the natural world has changed radically. Even as children and teenagers become more aware of global threats to the environment, their physical contact, their intimacy with nature, is fading. As one suburban fifth grader put it to me, in what has become the signature epigram of the children-and-nature movement: "I like to play indoors better 'cause that's where all the electrical outlets are."

His desire is not at all uncommon. In a typical week, only 6 percent of children ages nine to thirteen play outside on

Thanks to Erin Gately

their own... Urban, suburban, and even rural parents cite a number of everyday reasons why their children spend less time in nature than they themselves did, including disappearing access to natural areas, competition from television and computers, dangerous traffic, more homework, and other pressures. Most of all, parents cite fear of stranger-danger. Conditioned by round-the-clock news coverage, they believe in an epidemic of abductions by strangers, despite evidence that the number of child-snatchings (about a hundred a year) has remained roughly the same for two decades, and that the rates of violent crimes against young people have fallen to well below 1975 levels.

Yes, there are risks outside our homes. But there are also risks in raising children under virtual protective house arrest: threats to their independent judgment and value of place, to their ability to feel awe and wonder, to their sense of stewardship for the Earth — and, most immediately, threats to their psychological and physical health. The rapid increase in childhood obesity leads many health-care leaders to worry that the current generation of children may be the first since World War II to die at an earlier age than their parents. Getting kids outdoors more, riding bikes, running, swimming — and, especially, experiencing nature directly — could serve as an antidote to much of what ails the young.

The physical benefits are obvious, but other benefits are more subtle and no less important. Take the development of cognitive functioning. Factoring out other variables, studies of students in California and nationwide show that schools that use outdoor classrooms and other forms of experiential education produce significant student gains in social studies, science, language arts, and math. One 2005 study by the California Department of Education found that students in outdoor science programs improved their science testing scores by 27 percent.

And the benefits go beyond test scores. According to a range of studies, children in outdoor-education settings show increases in self-esteem, problem solving, and motivation to learn. ...Recent research also shows a positive correlation between the length of children's attention spans and direct experience in nature. Studies at the University of Illinois show that time in natural settings significantly reduces symptoms of attention-deficit (hyperactivity) disorder in children as young as age five. The research also shows the experience helps reduce negative stress and protects psychological well being, especially in children undergoing the most stressful life events.

Even without corroborating evidence or institutional help, many parents notice significant changes in their children's stress levels and hyperactivity when they spend time outside. "My son is still on Ritalin, but he's so much calmer in the outdoors that we're seriously considering moving to the mountains," one mother tells me. Could it simply be that he needs more physical activity? "No, he gets that, in sports," she says. Similarly, the back page of an October issue of *San Francisco* magazine displays a vivid photograph of a small boy, eyes wide with excitement and joy, leaping and running on a great expanse of California beach, storm clouds and towering waves behind him. A short article explains that the boy was hyperactive, he had been kicked out of his school, and his parents had not known what to do with him — but they had observed how nature engaged and soothed him. So for years they took their son to beaches, forests, dunes, and rivers to let nature do its work.

The photograph was taken in 1907. The boy was Ansel Adams.

◆ ◆ ◆

Studies show that, almost to a person, conservationists or environmentalists — whatever we want to call them — had some transcendent experience in nature when they were children. For some, the epiphanies took place in a national park; for others, in the clump of trees at the end of the cul-de-sac. But if experiences in nature are radically reduced for future generations, where will stewards of the Earth come from? A few months ago, I visited Ukiah, California, a mountain town nestled in the pines and fog. Ukiah is Spotted Owl Central, a town associated with the swirling controversy regarding logging, old growth, and endangered species. This is one of the most bucolic landscapes in our country, but local educators and parents report that Ukiah kids aren't going outside much anymore. So who will care about the spotted owl in ten or fifteen years?

....The future of children in nature has profound implications not only for the conservation of land but also for the direction of the environmental movement. If society embraces something as simple as the health benefits of nature experiences for children, it may begin to re-evaluate the worth of "the environment." While public-health experts have traditionally associated environmental health with the absence of toxic pollution, the definition fails to account for an equally valid consideration: how the environment can improve human health. Seen through that doorway, nature isn't a problem, it's the solution: environmentalism is essential to our own well-being. Howard Frumkin, director of the National Center for Environmental Health, points out that future research about the positive health effects of nature should be conducted in collaboration with architects, urban planners, park designers, and landscape architects. "Perhaps we will advise patients to take a few days in the country, to spend time gardening," he wrote in a 2001 *American Journal of Preventive Medicine* article, "or [we will] build hospitals in scenic locations, or plant gardens in rehabilitation centers. Perhaps the … organizations that pay for health care will come to fund such interventions, especially if they prove to rival pharmaceuticals in cost and efficacy." …

In every arena, from conservation and health to urban design and education, a growing children-and-nature movement will have no shortage of tools to bring about a world in which we leave no child inside — and no shortage of potential far-reaching benefits. Under the right conditions, cultural and political change can occur rapidly. The recycling and antismoking campaigns are our best examples of how social and political pressure can work hand-in-hand to create a societal transformation in just one generation. The children-and-nature movement has perhaps even greater potential — because it touches something even deeper within us, biologically and spiritually.

In January 2005, I attended a meeting of the Quivira Coalition, a New Mexico organization that brings together ranchers and environmentalists to find common ground. The coalition is now working on a plan to promote ranches as the new schoolyards. When my turn came to speak, I told the audience how, when I was a boy, I pulled out all those survey stakes in an attempt to keep the earthmovers at bay. Afterward, a rancher stood up. He was wearing scuffed boots. His aged jeans had never seen acid wash, only dirt and rock. His face was sunburned and creased. His drooping moustache was white, and he wore thick eyeglasses with heavy plastic frames, stained with sweat. "You know that story you told about pulling up stakes?" he said. "I did that when I was a boy, too."

The crowd laughed. I laughed.

And then the man began to cry. Despite his embarrassment, he continued to speak, describing the source of his sudden grief: that he might belong to one of the last generations of Americans to feel that sense of ownership of land and nature. The power of this movement lies in that sense, that special place in our hearts, those

woods where the bulldozers cannot reach. Developers and environmentalists, corporate CEOs and college professors, rock stars and ranchers may agree on little else, but they agree on this: no one among us wants to be a member of the last generation to pass on to its children the joy of playing outside in nature.

Published in the March/April 2007 issue of *Orion*. Mr. Louv is author of *Last Child in the Woods* (2008) and chairman and co-founder of Children & Nature Network, an organization helping build the movement to connect today's children and future generations to the natural world. www.childrenandnature.org

FOR THE CHILDREN
Gary Snyder

The rising hills, the slopes,
of statistics
lie before us.
the steep climb
of everything, going up,
up, as we all
go down.

In the next century
or the one beyond that,
they say,
are valleys, pastures,
we can meet there in peace
if we make it.

To climb these coming crests
one word to you, to
you and your children:

stay together
learn the flowers
go light

SESSION 4 — BUILDING HEALTHY COMMUNITIES
WHAT YOU CAN DO

If after completing this week's EcoChallenge you are motivated to take further action, consider the suggestions listed below. At your group's final gathering, you will have an opportunity to review the list again and commit to an action item.

Label each of these action items with a code representing its priority in your life.

N: Will do now
S: Will do within the next month
L: Will do within the next year
N/A: Not applicable to me

BEGIN RIGHT AWAY:

____ Go outside. Take a walk around your neighborhood and become familiar with your surroundings

____ Walk /bike to as many destinations as you can

____ Take the most direct route to a destination and group your trips

____ Support local, independent businesses

____ Clear the air! Don't let your car idle, just turn it off

____ Eat your landscape: support local farmers

____ Get to know your neighbors

____ Encourage your children to play outside; play with them

____ Other: _____

RESEARCH AND APPLY YOUR KNOWLEDGE:

____ Learn ways to get to destinations using public transportation

____ Identify the location of past and current landfills in your community (www.epa.gov/superfund/sites/). Share what you learn with other members of your community

____ Know what's in your water: http://projects.nytimes.com/toxic-waters/contaminants .If you're using well water, have it tested. If your drinking water is contaminated, reduce the duration of your showers to decrease your exposure to solvent inhalation

____ Know how your local air quality rates: www.scorecard.org

____ Find out if your community greens are sprayed and advocate for alternatives

____ Other: _____

REQUIRES MORE RESOURCES (TIME, ENERGY, MONEY, PEOPLE):

____ Organize carpools to school, work, shopping, and events

____ Start or join a community garden

____ Take an interest in local politics and influence decisions that affect your community's health

____ Organize or join a community tree planting event

____ Organize fun outdoor activities with your children such as hiking, biking, gardening and snow-shoeing. Invite other children and their parents.

____ Organize a group to take the Northwest Earth Institute course, *Choices for Sustainable Living*

____ Other: _____

SESSION 5

CURING CONSUMPTION

If I am what I have and if I lose what I have, who then am I?

— ERICH FROMM, GERMAN SOCIAL PSYCHOLOGIST AND PHILOSOPHER

SESSION GOALS

- To explore the life cycle of our "stuff" and how it impacts health

- To consider more sustainable alternatives to a consumer culture

- To examine our buying habits and learn ways to reduce personal consumption

SESSION BACKGROUND

Having considered some of the more direct links to health in previous sessions, the readings in this session look at health within the broader context of a consumer culture. While it is easy to see the connection between health and what we eat, drink and breathe, connecting the products we buy to our health can require some additional effort. The readings that follow help make the connections by examining the life cycle of our "stuff" and the impact on human and ecological health, suggesting that a change in cultural orientation is necessary to ensure a life-supporting planet for future generations.

This session begins with the short video, "The Story of Stuff" by Annie Leonard. Ms. Leonard follows her curiosity about how and where stuff is made and finds herself on a journey around the world, gaining insights into our roles as individuals in the global economy. In the next reading, an excerpt from "The Rise and Fall of Consumer Cultures," Eric Assadourian examines the culture of consumerism and offers an alternative vision that is life-sustaining. Duane Elgin explores this theme further in "Simplicity and Consumption."

One major byproduct of the cycle of "stuff" is waste and in particular, nonbiodegradable, petroleum-based plastic waste, which has grown along with our appetite for convenient, disposable products. Amanda Woods reports that this byproduct of consumer culture has now made its way into our oceans and marine life in "The Plastic Killing Fields."

In "A Cure for Consumption" Juliet Schor points to some positive consequences of the current economic downturn — people are making permanent changes in their spending habits that will ultimately lead to a healthier economy. In the final reading, "One Approach to Sustainability: Work Less," John de Graaf argues that a shorter work week would go a long way toward addressing the problems of consumer culture and restoring health to ourselves and our planet.

Circle Question

Is consumerism a malady to be cured?

Circle questions should move quickly — each member responds briefly without questions or comments from others. Facilitator guidelines are on page 6.

SUGGESTED DISCUSSION QUESTIONS

1. What was your reaction to "The Story of Stuff"? What are three things you can recall from watching it?

2. What goods that you once perceived as luxuries have become necessities to you in the last five years?

3. Do you ever feel you're on the treadmill Leonard describes in "The Story of Stuff?" How would a simpler lifestyle affect your overall health and well being?

4. Many of our "disposable" products make their way to the ocean. How can you personally reduce your contribution to the growing islands of plastic in our oceans?

5. Does the concept of "identity consumption" as defined by Duane Elgin resonate with you at all? Elaborate.

6. To what extent are you concerned about the shipping of e-waste to poorer countries? What are some possible solutions to this issue?

7. Juliet Schor points to a growing number of people who report a reduction in spending habits spurred by the economic downturn. Do you think this change in behavior will last? Why or why not?

8. Share an insight from this week's EcoChallenge.

Weekly EcoChallenge: Buying Less

Just don't buy it! Choose a realistic but challenging way to consume and reduce waste. For example, select one non-essential item you're in the habit of buying and give it up for the week (like bottled water or to-go coffee). Take it a step further and have a "buy nothing week" where you only buy essentials. Or visit the local resale shop to see what you might find there, instead of buying new.

To find out more about NWEI's annual EcoChallenge event, visit www.ecochallenge.org.

SUGGESTED READINGS AND RESOURCES

ORGANIZATIONS

Center for a New American Dream is an organization committed to shrinking the size of the American ecological footprint. To learn more go to www.newdream.org.

The Slow Movement aims to address the issue of time poverty. Go to www.slowmovement.com.

BOOKS

The Value of Nothing: How to Reshape Market Society and Redefine Democracy, Raj Patel (2010). Opening with Oscar Wilde's observation that "nowadays people know the price of everything and the value of nothing," Patel shows how our faith in prices as a way of valuing the world is misplaced. He reveals the hidden ecological and social costs of a hamburger (as much as $200), and asks how we came to have such markets in the first place.

Culture Jam: How to Reverse America's Suicidal Consumer Binge, by Kalle Lasn (2000). Lasn looks to break down the conventions of branding and advertising that constantly are telling us what should be most important, mainly wealth, possessions, and comfort.

ARTICLES

Please go to the Northwest Earth Institute website (www.nwei.org) for the most current list of articles relating to this session.

FILMS/DOCUMENTARIES

Consuming Kids focuses on the explosive growth of child marketing in the wake of deregulation. It shows how youth marketers have used the latest advances in psychology, anthropology, and neuroscience to transform American children into one of the most powerful and profitable consumer demographics in the world.

As you complete the weekly readings, please remember to fill out the course evaluation on page 7 or go to www.nwei.org/evaluation. Your comments will help NWEI improve the course. Thank you.

THE STORY OF STUFF
By Annie Leonard

www.thestoryofstuff.com

Please watch this short film before proceeding with the other readings. "The Story of Stuff" provides an overview of our consumer economy and sets the context for this session. The "host" of the video, Annie Leonard, takes an extremely complex topic — the global consumer economy — and boils it down into an eye-opening and accessible twenty-minute video . Even if you've watched it before, please take the time to watch it again, paying close attention to the health impacts that accompany the stages of consumption : extraction, production, distribution, consumption and waste.

Leonard is a tireless researcher and passionate activist for a more sustainable way of living. She does not hide her biases, and even if you disagree with her politics, we hope you will set that aside in order to gain important information and insights about the way "stuff" exists in our world.

THE RISE AND FALL OF CONSUMER CULTURE

By Eric Assadourian

Human beings are embedded in cultural systems, are shaped and constrained by their cultures, and for the most part act only within the cultural realities of their lives. The cultural norms, symbols, values, and traditions a person grows up with become "natural." Thus, asking people who live in consumer cultures to curb consumption is akin to asking them to stop breathing — they can do it for a moment, but then, gasping, they will inhale again. Driving cars, flying in planes, having large homes, using air conditioning…these are not decadent choices but simply natural parts of life — at least according to the cultural norms present in a growing number of consumer cultures in the world. Yet, while they seem natural to people who are part of those cultural realities, these patterns are neither sustainable nor innate manifestations of human nature. They have developed over several centuries and today are actively being reinforced and spread to millions of people in developing countries. Preventing the collapse of human civilization requires nothing less than a wholesale transformation of dominant cultural patterns. This transformation would reject consumerism — the cultural orientation that leads people to find meaning, contentment, and acceptance through what they consume — as taboo and establish in its place a new cultural framework centered on sustainability. In the process, a revamped understanding of "natural" would emerge: it would mean individual and societal choices that cause minimal ecological damage or, better yet, that restore Earth's ecological systems to health. Such a shift — something more fundamental than the adoption of new technologies or government policies, which are often regarded as the key drivers of a shift to sustainable societies — would radically reshape the way people understand and act in the world.

Transforming cultures is, of course, no small task. It will require decades of effort in which cultural pioneers — those who can step out of their cultural realities enough to critically examine them — work tirelessly to redirect key culture-shaping institutions: education, business, government, and the media, as well as social movements and long-standing human traditions. Harnessing these drivers of cultural change will be critical if humanity is to survive and thrive for centuries and millennia to come and prove that we are, indeed, "worth saving…. The Ecological

Footprint Indicator, which compares humanity's ecological impact with the amount of productive land and sea area available to supply key ecosystem services, shows that humanity now uses the resources and services of 1.3 Earths. (See Figure 1.) In other words, people are using about a third more of Earth's capacity than is available, undermining the resilience of the very ecosystems on which humanity depends.

In 2005 the Millennium Ecosystem Assessment (MA), a comprehensive review of scientific research that involved 1,360 experts from 95 countries, reinforced these findings. It found that some 60 percent of ecosystem services — climate regulation, the provision of fresh water, waste treatment, food from fisheries, and many other services — were being degraded or used unsustainably. The findings were so unsettling that the MA Board warned that "human activity is putting such strain on the natural functions of Earth that the ability of the planet's ecosystems to sustain future generations can no longer be taken for granted."

The shifts in one particular ecosystem service — climate regulation — are especially disturbing. After remaining at stable levels for the past 1,000 years at about 280 parts per million, atmospheric concentrations of carbon dioxide (CO_2) are now at 385 parts per million, driven by a growing human population consuming ever more fossil fuels, eating more meat, and converting more land to agriculture and urban areas. The Intergovernmental Panel on Climate Change found that climate change due to human activities is causing major disruptions in Earth's systems. If greenhouse gas emissions are not curbed, disastrous changes will occur in the next century.

And climate change is just one of the many symptoms of excessive consumption levels. Air pollution, the average loss of 7 million hectares of forests per year, soil erosion,

Figure 1. Humanity's Ecological Footprint, 1961-2005

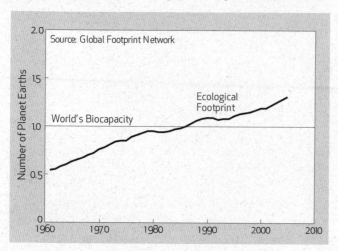

DO HIGH CONSUMPTION LEVELS IMPROVE HUMAN WELL-BEING?

Ultimately, whether high consumption levels make people better off is irrelevant if they lead to the degradation of Earth's systems, as ecological decline will undermine human well-being for the majority of society in the long term. But even assuming this threat were not looming, there is strong evidence that higher levels of consumption do not significantly increase the quality of life beyond a certain point, and may even reduce it. First, psychological evidence suggests that it is close relationships, a meaningful life, economic security, and health that contribute most to well-being. While there are marked improvements in happiness when people at low levels of income earn more (as their economic security improves and their range of opportunities grows), as incomes increase this extra earning power converts less effectively into increased happiness. In part, this may stem from people's tendency to habituate to the consumption level they are exposed to. Goods that were once perceived as luxuries can over time be seen as entitlements or even necessities.

By the 1960s, for instance, the Japanese already viewed a fan, a washing machine, and electric rice cooker as essential goods for a satisfactory living standard. In due course, a car, an air conditioner, and a color television were added to the list of "essentials." And in the United States, 83 percent of people saw clothes dryers as a necessity in 2006. Even products around only a short time quickly become viewed as necessities. Half of Americans now think they must have a mobile phone, and one third of them see a high-speed Internet connection as essential.

A high-consumption lifestyle can also have many side effects that do not improve well-being, from increased work stress and debt, to more illness and a greater risk of death. Each year roughly half of all deaths worldwide are caused by cancers, cardiovascular and lung diseases, diabetes, and auto accidents. Many of these deaths are caused, or at least largely influenced, by individual consumption choices such as smoking, being sedentary, eating too few fruits and vegetables, and being overweight. Today 1.6 billion people around the world are overweight or obese, lowering their quality of life and shortening their lives, for the obese, by 3 to 10 years on average.

Source: *State of the World 2010*

the annual production of over 100 million tons of hazardous waste, abusive labor practices driven by the desire to produce more and cheaper consumer goods, obesity, increasing time stress — the list could go on and on. All these problems are often treated separately, even as many of their roots trace back to current consumption. While consumerism is now found in nearly all cultures, it is not without consequences. On this finite planet, defining success and happiness through how much a person consumes is not sustainable. Moreover, it is abundantly clear that this cultural orientation did not just happen to appear as a byproduct of growing incomes. It was engineered over several centuries.

Today, since consumerism has been internalized by many societies, it is self-perpetuating to some extent, yet institutions within society — including businesses, the media, governments, and educational facilities — continue to prop up this cultural orientation. These institutions also are actively working to expand markets around the world for new consumer goods and services. Understanding the role of these institutional drivers will be essential in order to cultivate new cultures of sustainability. ….

Considering the social and ecological costs that come with consumerism, it makes sense to intentionally shift to a cultural paradigm where the norms, symbols, values, and traditions encourage just enough consumption to satisfy human well-being while directing more human energy toward practices that help to restore planetary well-being.

In a 2006 interview, Catholic priest and ecological philosopher Thomas Berry noted that "we might summarize our present human situation by the simple statement: In the 20th century, the glory of the human has become the desolation of the Earth. And now, the desolation of the Earth is becoming the destiny of the human. From here on, the primary judgment of all human institutions, professions, and programs and activities will be determined by the extent to which they inhibit, ignore, or foster a mutually enhancing human-Earth relationship." Berry made it clear that a tremendous shift is necessary in society's institutions, in its very cultures, if humans are to thrive as a species long into the future. Institutions will have to be fundamentally oriented on sustainability.

How can this be done? In an analysis on places to intervene in a system, environmental scientist and systems analyst Donella Meadows explained that the most effective leverage point for changing a system is to change the paradigm of the system — that is to say, the shared ideas or basic assumptions around which the system functions. In the case of the consumerism paradigm, the assumptions that need to change include that more stuff makes people happier, that perpetual growth is good, that humans are separate from nature, and that nature is a stock of resources to be exploited for human purposes.

Although paradigms are difficult to change and societies will resist efforts to do so, the result of such a change can be a dramatic transformation of the system. Yes, altering a system's rules (with legislation, for instance) or its flow rates (with taxes or subsidies) can change a system too, but not as fundamentally. These will typically produce only incremental changes.

Today, more systemic change is needed. Cultural systems vary widely, as noted earlier, and so too would sustainable cultures. Some may use norms, taboos, rituals, and other social tools to reinforce sustainable life choices; others may lean more on institutions, laws, and technologies. But regardless of which tools are used, and the specific result, there would be common themes across sustainable cultures. Just as a consumerism paradigm encourages people to define their well-being through their consumption patterns, a sustainability paradigm would work to find an alternative set of aspirations and reinforce this through cultural institutions and drivers.

Ecological restoration would be a leading theme. It should become "natural" to find value and meaning in life through how much a person helps restore the planet rather than how much that individual earns, how large a home is, or how many gadgets someone has.

Equity would also be a strong theme. As it is the richest who have some of the largest ecological impacts, and the very poorest who, often by necessity, are forced into unsustainable behaviors like deforestation in a search for fuelwood, more equitable distribution of resources within society could help to curb some of the worst ecological impacts. Recent research also shows that societies that are more equitable have less violence, better health, higher literacy levels, lower incarceration rates, less obesity, and lower levels of teen pregnancy — all substantial bonus dividends that would come with cultivating this value…. A host of social movements are starting to form that directly or indirectly tackle issues of sustainability. Hundreds of thousands of organizations are working, often quietly on their own and unknown to each other, on the many essential aspects of building sustainable cultures — such as social and environmental justice, corporate responsibility, restoration of ecosystems, and government reform. "This unnamed movement is the most diverse movement the world has ever seen," explains environmentalist Paul Hawken. "The very word movement I think is too small to describe it." Together these have the power to redirect the momentum of consumerism and provide a vision of a sustainable future that appeals to everyone. Efforts to promote working less and living more simply, the Slow Food movement, Transition Towns, and ecovillages are all inspiring and empowering people to redirect both their own lives and broader society toward sustainability.

Finally, cultural traditions are starting to be reoriented toward sustainability. New ecofriendly ways to celebrate rituals are being established, for instance, and are becoming socially acceptable. Family size norms are starting to shift. Lost traditions, like the wise guidance of elders, are being rediscovered and used to support the shift to sustainability. And religious organizations are starting to use their mighty influence to tackle environmental issues — printing *Green Bibles*, encouraging their congregations to conserve energy, investing institution funds responsibly, and taking a stance against abuses of Creation, such as razing forests and blowing up mountaintops for coal. Perhaps in a century or two, extensive efforts to pioneer a new cultural orientation will no longer be needed as people will have internalized many of these new ideas, seeing sustainability — rather than consumerism — as "natural." Until then, networks of cultural pioneers will be needed to push institutions to proactively and intentionally accelerate this shift. Anthropologist Margaret Mead is often quoted as saying: "Never doubt that a small group of thoughtful, committed citizens can change the world. Indeed, it's the only thing that ever has." With many interconnected citizens energized, organized, and committed to spreading a sustainable way of life, a new cultural paradigm can take hold — one that will allow humanity to live better lives today and long into the future.

Excerpt from *World Watch State of the World 2010*. Erik Assadourian is a Senior Researcher at the Worldwatch Institute and Project Director of State of the World 2010.

SIMPLICITY AND CONSUMPTION

By Duane Elgin

To live sustainably, it is vital that we each decide how much is "enough." Simplicity is a double-edged sword: Living with either too little or too much will diminish our capacity to realize our potentials. Balance occurs when there is neither material excess nor deficit. To find this in our everyday lives requires that we understand the difference between our needs and wants. "Needs" are things that are essential to our survival and our growth. "Wants" are those things that are extra — that gratify our psychological desires. For example, we *need* shelter in order to survive; we may *want* a huge house with many extra rooms that are seldom used. We *need* basic medical care; we may *want* cosmetic surgery to disguise the fact that we are getting older. We *need* functional clothing; we may *want* frequent changes in clothing style to reflect the latest fashion. We *need* a nutritious and well-balanced diet; we may *want* to eat at expensive restaurants. We *need* transportation; we may *want* a new Mercedes. Only when we are clear about what we need and what we want can we begin to pare away the excess and find a middle path between extremes. Discovering this balance in everyday life is central to our learning, and no one else can find it for us.

The hallmark of a balanced simplicity is that our lives become clearer, more direct, less pretentious, and less complicated. We are then empowered by our material circumstances rather than enfeebled or distracted by them. Excess in either direction — too much or too little — is complicating. If we are totally absorbed in the struggle to accumulate, then our capacity to participate wholeheartedly and enthusiastically in life is diminished. Four consumption criteria go to the very heart of the issue of balanced consumption:

• Does what I own or buy promote activity, self-reliance, and involvement, or does it induce passivity and dependence?

Thanks to Janet Sass McDermott

- Are my consumption patterns basically satisfying, or do I buy much that serves no real need?
- How tied are my present job and lifestyle to installment payments, maintenance and repair costs, and the expectations of others?
- Do I consider the impact of my consumption patterns on other people and on the Earth?

This compassionate approach to consumption stands in stark contrast to the modern view that consumption is a critical expression of our personal identity. Too often we equate our identity with that which we consume. When we engage in "identity consumption," we become possessed by our possessions, we are consumed by that which we consume. Our identity becomes not a freestanding, authentic expression in the moment, but a material mask that we have constructed so as to present a more appealing image for others to see. The vastness of who we are is them compressed into an ill-fitting and awkward shell that obscures our uniqueness and natural beauty. We begin a never-ending search for a satisfying experience of identity. We look beyond ourselves for the next thing that will make us happy: a new car, a new wardrobe, a new job, a new hairstyle, a new house, and so on. Instead of lasting satisfaction, we find only temporary gratification. After the initial gratification subsides, we must begin again — looking for the next thing that, this time, will bring some measure of enduring satisfaction. But the search is both endless and hopeless, because it is continually directed away from the "self" that is doing the searching.

If we pause in our search and begin to discover that our true identity is much larger than any that can be fashioned through even the most opulent levels of material consumption, then the entire driving force behind our attempts at "identity consumption" is fundamentally transformed. It is transformative to withdraw voluntarily from the preoccupations with the material rat race of accumulation and instead accept our natural experience — unadorned by superfluous goods — as sufficient unto itself. It is a radical simplicity to affirm that our happiness cannot be purchased, no matter how desperately the advertiser may want us to believe the fiction that we will never be happy or adequate without this or that product. It is a radical simplicity when we accept our bodies as they are — when we affirm that each of us is endowed with a dignity, beauty, and character whose natural expression is infinitely more interesting and engaging that any imagined identity we might construct with layers of clothes and cosmetics.

This excerpt is from *Voluntary Simplicity: Toward a Way of Life that is Outwardly Simple, Inwardly Rich*, Second Revised Edition, Harper-Collins Publishers, 2010. Duane Elgin is an internationally recognized speaker, author, and social visionary who pioneered the "voluntary simplicity" movement in the 1980s.

THE PLASTIC KILLING FIELDS

By Amanda Woods

In one of the few places on Earth where people can rarely be found, the human race has well and truly made its mark. In the middle of the Pacific Ocean lies a floating garbage patch twice the size of Britain. A place where the water is filled with six times as much plastic as plankton. This plastic-plankton soup is entering the food chain and heading for your dinner table.

For hundreds of years, sailors and fisherman have known to avoid the area between the Equator and 50 degrees north latitude about halfway between California and Hawaii. As one of the ocean's deserts, the North Pacific Subtropical Gyre lacks the wind that sailors need to survive, as well as the nutrients to support large fish or the men who hunt them.

But 10 years ago, Captain Charles Moore took a short cut through the airless doldrums in his catamaran, Alguita, and caught sight of something that changed his life. As he looked out at what should have been a clear blue ocean, Moore saw a sea of plastic. As far as he could see, day after day, were bottles, wrappers and fragments of plastic in every color.

Historically, the ocean's circular currents have led to accumulation of flotsam and jetsam in the subtropical high, where the waste has biodegraded with the help of marine micro-organisms. But since humans developed a material designed for durability, which can survive exposure to any bacteria, the gyre has been filling with a substance it can't get rid of. Rather than biodegrading, plastic photodegrades, breaking down in the sunlight into smaller and smaller pieces. But no matter how small it gets, it's still plastic, and causes havoc when it enters the stomachs of marine life.

Ian Kiernan, the Australian who founded Clean Up the World, started his environmental campaign 20 years ago after he became appalled by the amount of rubbish he saw on an around-the-world solo yacht race. He'll never forget the first time he saw the gyre.

"It was just filled with things like furniture, fridges, plastic containers, cigarette lighters, plastic bottles, light globes, televisions and fishing nets," Kiernan says.

"It's all so durable it floats. It's just a major problem."

He picks up an ashtray filled with worn-down coloured pieces of plastic. "This is the contents of a fleshy-footed shearwater's stomach," he says. "They go to the ocean to fish but there ain't no fish — there's plastic. They then regurgitate it down the necks of their fledglings and it kills them. After the birds decompose, the plastic gets washed back into the ocean where it can kill again. It's a form of ghost fishing, where it goes on and on."

With gyres in each of the oceans, connected by debris highways, the problem isn't restricted to the North Pacific Gyre. It is estimated there are more than 13,000 pieces of plastic litter on every square kilometre of the ocean surface.

The United Nations Environment Program says plastic is accountable for the deaths of more than a million seabirds and more than 100,000 marine mammals such as whales, dolphins and seals every year. A Dutch study in the North Sea of fulmar seabirds concluded 95 percent of the birds had plastic in their stomachs. More than 1600 pieces were found in the stomach of one bird in Belgium.

Since his first encounter with the gyre in 1997, Moore has returned several times and created the Algalita Marine Research Foundation to study the problem. The Canadian filmmaker Ian Connacher joined Moore in 2005 and again last year to film the garbage patch for his documentary, I Am Plastic. After a week of sailing from Long Beach, California, Connacher was not prepared for what he saw.

"Charlie once found a mile-long trail of Taco Bell wrappers which had plastic in them. I didn't see anything like that, but that's not the point, because it's the little bits that are really making it a plastic soup," Connacher says.

"The most menacing part is those little bits of plastic start looking like food for certain animals, or the filter feeders don't have any choice, they just pick them up." Then there's the plastic that doesn't float. Greenpeace reports that about 70 percent of the plastic that makes it to the ocean sinks to the bottom, where it can smother marine life. Greenpeace says Dutch scientists have found 600,000 tonnes of discarded plastic on the bottom of the North Sea alone.

A study by the Japanese geochemist Hideshige Takada and his colleagues at Tokyo University in 2001 found that plastic polymers act like a sponge for resilient poisons such as DDT and polychlorinated biphenyls. Takada's team found non-water-soluble toxic chemicals can be found in plastic in levels as high as a million times their concentration in water.

As small pieces of plastic are mistaken for fish eggs and other food by marine life, these toxins enter the food chain. Even without this extra toxic load, eating plastic can be hazardous to the health.

In 2002, a study of hermaphrodite fish led Canadian scientists to link oestrogen in water to abnormal sex organs in fish. Several plastic additives have been found to mimic oestrogen. Some experts, such as Frederick vom Saal, a professor of biological sciences at Missouri University, say declining fertility rates in humans could be linked to exposure to synthetic oestrogen in plastics.

Some of the ocean's plastic arrives over the side of a ship as litter, and some is the result of containers falling into the ocean. But Greenpeace says about 80 percent of plastic found at sea is washed out from the land.

The journal Science last year predicted seafood stocks would collapse by 2048 if overfishing and pollution continued.

Greenpeace says embracing the three Rs — reduce, re-use and recycle — would help tackle the problem. Plastic recycling is lagging well behind paper and cardboard, as people are confused about what recycling is available in their areas. There are other challenges for plastic recycling, such as the fact that it can release toxic chemicals into the atmosphere, and that it is more expensive to recycle some plastic than to create a new product from petrochemicals.

The use of bioplastics could help reduce the amount with which we are coating the planet. Traditional petrochemical-based plastics are non-degradable and non-renewable; degradable plastic breaks into smaller pieces in UV light but remains plastic; and there are two kinds of biodegradable plastic that break down in compost — one from a petrochemical resource, the other from a renewable resource such as corn or wheat, which is known as bioplastic.

A PICTURE SAYS A THOUSAND WORDS

For many of us the impact of consumer choices is "out of sight, out of mind." Photographer Chris Jordan's images shown in the links below remind us that there is no "away."

Midway: Message from the Gyre
www.youtube.com/watch?v=gbqJ6FLfaJc

Intolerable Beauty:
Portraits of American Mass Consumption
www.chrisjordan.com/gallery/
intolerable/#cellphones2

Dr Katherine Dean, of the CSIRO, says corporate firms have become interested in bioplastic over the past three years.

"When oil prices soared in 2005, that changed a lot of people's perspective, because bioplastic became quite cost-competitive," she says. "All of a sudden it wasn't just about doing the right thing."

In 2001 CSIRO researchers were involved in the development of a corn-based bioplastic that would provide the foundation for the company Plantic Technologies, which developed biodegradable plastic for everything from food and beverage packaging to medical, agricultural and sporting applications.

The chief executive of Plantic, Grant Dow, says once composted, the plastic would become nothing more than carbon dioxide and water.

"For all intents and purposes, it looks like plastic and feels like plastic and does the same thing as plastic in the application," he says.

"It will only biodegrade in the presence of heat, moisture and bacteria, so it will sit in your cupboard pretty much indefinitely, but when the bacteria get to it in compost, that's it. It's gone."

While researchers continue to develop bioplastics, there's no doubt the new generation of polymers can make a difference in day-to-day living. Already supermarkets in Britain, such as Marks & Spencer, Sainsbury's and Tesco, have introduced bioplastic packaging, and food companies are embracing the concept.

Connacher believes as consumers learn more about the situation, many will respond positively. "We think products are going to be recycled, but they're not. We have become irresponsible with the way we use a lot of things, particularly disposable products. "

Published in the *Sydney Morning Herald*, December 29, 2007
smh.com.au

A CURE FOR CONSUMPTION

By Juliet Schor

As good economic news finally begins to surface, there's a temptation to assume that the United States can revert to business as usual. A dash of financial regulation, a pinch of cash for state and local governments and the unemployed, and we'll be back on track with our debt-driven consumer economy. Many assume that a debt and consumption-led process is the only way to create jobs, incomes, and well-being — even if household balance sheets are already stretched.

But that's not what builds wealth, and it's not how economies work. Another solution is emerging as hard economic times have dovetailed with the sustainability movement. People are thinking beyond the big-box stores, inventing low-impact, do-it-yourself lifestyles that may hold the model for a 21st-century economy. While the shift away from debt-fueled consumption represents a major change for the US economy, it doesn't need to be wrenching for American households.

It is true that consumers became the engine of economic growth in the United States. Until the recent economic crisis, the fraction of total output dedicated to consumption of goods and services was rising significantly, from 63 percent in 1960 to 70 percent in 2008. In recent decades, much of that consumption was made possible by credit. In the 1980s and '90s, debt payments represented about 10 percent of disposable income — but soared to just under 14 percent in the run-up to the crash. There are a number of reasons why households took on so much debt, but declining real wages and rising home prices were key. People needed to borrow to buy a home — or just to keep consumption from falling.

But since the autumn of 2008, household indebtedness has reversed sharply. Total credit outstanding and the debt service ratio declined, while personal saving has risen sharply. People wisely took action to limit financial liabilities in an environment of high unemployment and uncertainty.

Will it last? One side points to the revival of GDP growth, rising consumer confidence, and the uptick in consumer spending. But demand has been dominated by luxuries purchased by high-income households, and there are too few to sustain the recovery.

The other view is supported by a number of surveys showing that people have been permanently affected by the downturn. In April [2010], the Gallup Poll found that 57 percent of Americans were spending less, and this fraction has been growing over the past year. Thirty-eight percent of this group reports that their habits will be permanent. The same poll found that after years of near-parity, more people enjoy saving than spending. In addition, the traumas of unemployment, bankruptcy, and foreclosure experienced by tens of millions will affect willingness to spend and borrow for decades.

If frugality is the "new normal," what are the consequences for the economy? Don't we need robust growth in spending to create jobs and prosperity? This view has been overly represented in the popular media, which relies heavily on economists with close ties to the retail sector. These are the folks who anxiously read the tea leaves on Black Friday, during the August back-to-school sales, and when retail sales reports are released.

But not all spending is the same. Do Americans need more cellphones, cheap air travel, and junk food?

A growing number of people are answering that question in the negative, pioneering a lifestyle that is less focused on buying. They're devotees of "economies of re-use and re-cycling," and frequent sites such as Craigslist and freecycle.org, which organizes free exchanges of unwanted goods. They're also going beyond re-sale to Web-facilitated sharing of durable goods such as tools, appliances, and even vehicles. And they're starting "time banks" in which people trade services locally, rather than purchasing them from professionals. One of my graduate students is getting her data analyzed in exchange for preparing meals.

What people are losing in consumer goods, they are making up in creative activity and social connection. Vegetable gardening has exploded since the recession began. Urban poultry is all the rage. Do-it-yourself activity is also extending to small-scale electricity generation and home construction using eco-friendly materials. People are coming together to help each other with their projects, consciously building social capital and interdependence. These cultural pioneers often work limited hours in the market, replacing lost income with home-produced goods and services.

Of course, there have been similar movements since the 19th century, and none has stopped the creep of consumer culture. But today, with more than 26 million Americans currently under or unemployed, the basic economic landscape has changed: cash is scarce and time is plentiful. Ecological constraints point in the same direction. Growth will re-ignite increases in food and energy prices, which in turn enhance the appeal of this lower-impact, lower-cost lifestyle.

If we're turning away from McMansions and designer handbags, what should we be turning toward? Our long-term economic well-being depends centrally on productivity performance, which is closely tied to investment. Investment, whether it's in machinery, education, or natural resources, increases future wealth by building assets and enhancing productivity. Unfortunately, gross domestic investment has been falling since 2006, and has barely risen since 2002.

Can a shift toward investment — especially toward education, alternative energy, and ecological restoration — generate enough employment and consumption for the bottom 40 percent of the population who don't yet have enough? Not alone. But then, the trickle-down growth approach can't either. Combining new lifestyles at the household level with new priorities at the national scale is emerging as the smart way to move forward. To make that happen, our economic conversation should not just be about how much, but also, what, for whom, and how?

Published in *The Boston Globe*, May 30, 2010. Juliet Schor is the author of *Plenitude: The New Economics of True Wealth*, and a professor of sociology at Boston College.

E-WASTE: WHERE DOES IT GO?
Compiled by NWEI staff

Humans have the funny idea that when you get rid of something, it's gone.

— Elizabeth Grossman

The use of electronic products has grown substantially over the past two decades, changing the way and the speed in which we communicate and how we get information and entertainment. For many, electronics are part of modern life — cell phones, laptops, TVs and a growing number of gadgets. Every year we buy new, updated equipment to support our needs — there are upwards of 300 million computers and one billion cell phones produced every year.

Electronics are the fastest growing waste stream in many countries. All of these electronics become obsolete or unwanted, often within 2-3 years of purchase. Electronics are complex devices which are made of a wide variety of material constituents. Some of the materials, such as lead, nickel, cadmium, and mercury, pose risks to human health and to the environment when disposed.

In 2005, the Environmental Protection Agency estimated that between 26 to 37 million computers became obsolete. Along with computers, TVs, VCRs, cell phones, and monitors — an estimated 304 million electronics — were removed from US households in 2005, with about two-thirds of those still in working order, according to Consumer Electronics Association (CEA) estimates. Although used electronics represent less than two percent of the municipal solid waste stream, if we continue to replace old or outdated electronic equipment at our current rate that percentage will likely grow. In 2005, used or unwanted electronics amounted to approximately 1.9 to 2.2 million tons. Of that, about 1.5 to 1.8 million tons were primarily disposed in landfills, and only 345,000 to 379,000 tons were recycled. Additionally, illegal exports to the world's poorest countries — China, India and Africa — for dismantling is a growing concern.

To learn more about e-waste, go to:

- The Basel Action Network www.ban.org

- Elizabeth Grossman traces the trail of high-tech waste in her book *High Tech Trash: Digital Devices, Hidden Toxics, and Human Health.*

- A 60 Minutes video highlights this issue in a twenty minute video clip entitled *Following The Trail of Toxic e-waste*: www.cbsnews.com/stories/2008/11/06/60minutes/main4579229.shtml

WHAT CAN YOU DO?

- First, ask if you really need it before buying something new. Consider a product's lifecycle and where it will ultimately end up before making a new purchase. Can you buy a refurbished one instead? Can you make do with the one you have or without?

- If you're thinking about replacing a broken electronic item, see if the one you have can be fixed first. If not, visit www.e-stewards.org to find a reputable electronics recycler near you.

- Tell your representatives to support take-back programs, stricter e-waste regulations and the reduction of toxic chemicals in products.

- Contact manufacturers to demand product-take back programs and more products that can be easily upgraded, rather than replaced.

Sources:, e-stewards.com, Environmental Protection Agency,

ONE APPROACH TO SUSTAINABILITY: WORK LESS

By John de Graaf

About six years ago, I addressed the annual state conference of the Associated Recyclers of Wisconsin, an organization of private and public waste managers. The topic of my talk, "Haste Makes Waste," was focused on overwork and overconsumption. I told the assembled solid-waste handlers, "if you want to reduce landfills, reduce working hours."

I argued that the long hours we in the United States work — some 300 more per year than western Europeans — mean we are more likely to rely on "convenience" and disposable items, such as heavily-packaged fast foods and single-use goods. I told my audience that many people had told me they were "too pressed for time even to recycle." Moreover, our long work hours allow us to produce and buy more and more "stuff," resulting in a greater pressure on resources and an inevitably stream of more waste.

A few members of the audience told me they agreed with my remarks, but I'm sure most thought I was pretty far out. Since then, the arguments for cutting working time to save the planet have only gotten more compelling.

I'm all for the new greener technologies and alternative energy strategies, but by themselves, they won't stop climate change or create a sustainable society. To do so, we need to think outside the box and apply whole systems-thinking to the ecological and social problems we face. To create a sustainable society, we'll need to work less to have more of what we truly need: time.

EUROPE — VIVE LA DIFFERENCE!

With their long vacations and far shorter working hours, Europeans are consistently far healthier than Americans — after the age of 50, they are only about half as likely to suffer from chronic illnesses such as heart disease, Type 2 diabetes, hypertension and even cancer. They are only half as likely to suffer from depression and anxiety, and they spend only half as much on average as we do for health care. Studies show their better health results from more exercise, more socializing with friends and families, less stress and more sleep; all of these are made possible by having more time.

Europeans are not only more personally sustainable (they live longer!), but they are also more environmentally sustainable. On average, they produce only about half the amount of air pollution, use half as much energy and produce half as much solid waste and greenhouse carbon per capita as we do; all while enjoying a similar material lifestyle. Their average "ecological footprint," at 12 acres per person, is also about half that of ours. They are far from perfect (since their lifestyles still would require two and half planets if reproduced everywhere), but their ecological impact is far less than ours.

A December, 2006, study by the Center for Economic and Policy Research provided strong evidence that if Americans were to reduce their working hours to European levels, they could drastically cut their energy use by as much as 26 percent, nearly meeting key Kyoto climate change targets. This is a massive reduction. Combine this with advances in clean energy technology, and we could reduce our impacts even further.

The study argued that by reducing work hours, Americans would reduce the energy used for transportation (with more time, Europeans are far more likely to walk, bike or take public transit), and even more importantly, that they would reduce the energy necessary for the production of goods — as Americans trade time for money, they would consume and produce less.

THE FOUR-DAY WEEK

In response to escalating fuel costs, many companies are now considering going to a four-day work week. They believe this will save large sums on commuter fuel expenses and reduce traffic congestion. The problem is that they mean four 10-hour days. But for many American families in which both parents work, such long days will intensify daily stress.

Families will find less time to take care of tasks on the home front, or to exercise, eat properly and so forth; and families with young children will be hit particularly hard — imagine leaving children in daycare 10 or more hours a day. The health impacts could be severe. There will be increased pressure to reduce commute times (since the work day is already so long), encouraging more high-energy (automobile) commuting to get to and from work faster so as to have more time at home. Moreover, businesses will see a clear decline in hourly productivity, since fatigue sets in rapidly after eight hours on the job.

The real solution to this problem is to go to a four-day workweek of eight-hour days. Total production would be reduced slightly, but this will make us more sustainable. The commuting/energy benefits of the four-day week would be kept, without the negatives. We could expect significant reductions in energy and resource use, and in health problems and health care costs. Talk about a win-win situation! The Center for a New American Dream, a Maryland non-profit, has had such a 32-hour work week for 10 years, with excellent results for productivity, creativity and worker morale.

VACATION TIME AS A FIRST STEP TOWARD SHORTER HOURS

In 2002, together with a group of colleagues, I started TAKE BACK YOUR TIME to promote the idea of trading gains in productivity for time instead of stuff. In our view, such a strategy would leave Americans healthier, happier, and more connected to each other, their communities and the environment. Increasingly, the evidence is mounting that we were on the right track. We are now working on campaign to pass a law in the United States guaranteeing paid vacation for workers (the United States is currently the only industrial nation without such a law). But the campaign is about more than passing the law; it's about generating a new national dialogue about the importance of time.

This article was posted on www.Worldchanging.org on June 20, 2008. John de Graaf is the national coordinator of Take Back Your Time, an organization challenging time poverty and overwork in the United States and Canada (see www.timeday.org) and a frequent speaker on issues of overwork and over-consumption in America. He is co-author of the best-selling *Affluenza: The All-Consuming Epidemic* (Berrett-Koehler, 2001/2005).

To live more simply is to live more purposefully
and with a minimum of needless distraction.

— DUANE ELGIN, AUTHOR OF *VOLUNTARY SIMPLICITY*

SESSION 5 — CURING CONSUMPTION
WHAT YOU CAN DO

If after completing this week's EcoChallenge you are motivated to take further action, consider the suggestions listed below. At your group's final gathering, you will have an opportunity to review the list again and commit to an action item.

Label each of these action items with a code representing its priority in your life.

N: Will do now
S: Will do within the next month
L: Will do within the next year
N/A: Not applicable to me

BEGIN RIGHT AWAY:

____ Recycle, but reduce and reuse first

____ Ask if a new purchase is a want or need, and think twice if it's a want. Reduce waste by consuming less

____ Walk, bike, run, play

____ Unplug and connect with those around you

____ Power down electronics: leave them off or unplugged when not in use

____ Give an experience as a gift such as tickets to an events or activitiy (or better still, time with you!) instead of stuff

____ Reduce your exposure to advertising: avoid commercial media, cancel catalogues (www.catalogchoice.org/)

____ Pay attention to where the stuff you buy comes from.-check labels, ask questions

____ Select goods that are durable and have traveled fewer miles

____ Other: _____

RESEARCH AND APPLY YOUR KNOWLEDGE:

____ Determine your ecological footprint, which assesses how well we are living within the limits of one planet. Go to Global Footprint Network (www.footprintnetwork.org)

____ Re-evaluate your priorities and make time for what counts. Write it down and put it somewhere that you'll see it!

____ Support fair trade products (www.greenamericatoday.org/programs/fairtrade/products/index.cfm)

____ Try to fix broken products before you throw them out

____ Find ways to sell, donate or recycle things you no longer need rather than just throwing them out. Check out www.freecycle.org

____ Support cradle-to-cradle products (www.mbdc.com/detail.aspx?linkid=2&sublink=8 ; check C2C certified products link)

____ Learn where to recycle e-waste (www.e-stewards.org)

____ Other: _____

REQUIRES MORE RESOURCES (TIME, ENERGY, MONEY, PEOPLE):

____ Avoid disposables: use real cups, cloth napkins, reusable shopping bags, and rags for cleaning

____ Extend the life of your clothes by line-drying them outside or using a drying rack inside. Drying inside also cools your living space in the summer and humidifies it in the winter

____ Talk to others about your experiences as you wean yourself from the habit of excessive consumption

____ Take vacations and leave your work behind

____ Organize a group to take the Northwest Earth Institute's *Voluntary Simplicity* course

____ Other: _____

SESSION 6

HEALTHY PLANET, HEALTHY SELF

The frog does not drink up the pond in which he lives.

— Teton Sioux

SESSION GOALS

- To examine the role of biodiversity in maintaining human health

- To become aware of the threats to biodiversity and actions we can take to protect it

- To consider ways in which we can protect future generations' health and well-being

- To become aware of the health impacts of climate change and identify ways to reduce our carbon footprint

SESSION BACKGROUND

The focus of this session widens to consider health within the context of Earth's dynamic and life-sustaining ecosystems. The readings explore the importance of biodiversity, the health of the oceans, climate change and the interplay between the forces of nature, all of which affect our individual and collective health. They urge us to broaden their thinking about health to include the ecological realities in which we live. They contend that when we realize that our own health and well-being is ultimately dependent on the health of the planet, we will make choices that will support life on our planet.

In the first reading, "Think Like an Ocean," Andi McDaniel ponders our inability to comprehend the extent to which the oceans are declining. According to McDaniel, if we are to restore our oceans, we must first stretch our imaginations beyond what we can see. In the next reading, "Embedded in Nature: Human Health and Biodiversity," professors Eric Chivian and Aaron S. Bernstein describe the complex web of life we inhabit, and voice their concerns about the decline of biodiversity and its consequences for functioning ecosystem services. One major threat to ecosystem services is climate change, as described in "Climate Change and Health Vulnerabilities" by Juan Almendares and Paul R. Epstein.

The last three readings connect these global themes to more personal stories and reflections. In "Restoring Nature, Restoring Self" Francesca Lyman offers an inspiring story of mutual healing. In "3 Bets" Sandra Steingraber weaves her unique story as a cancer survivor, ecologist, and mother into her search for answers about health and the environment. She offers an inspiring vision of an emerging environmental human rights movement. In the final reading, an excerpt from *Hunting for Hope*, Scott Russell Sanders shares his thoughts on hope and despair, offering wisdom and practical advice on maintaining hope in a changing world.

Circle Question

Since you began this course, have you made any significant changes related to health and the environment? Explain.

Circle questions should move quickly —each member responds briefly without questions or comments from others. Facilitator guidelines are on page 6.

SUGGESTED DISCUSSION QUESTIONS

1. Respond to Andi McDaniel's statement, "It's harder to identify with tuna."

2. What images, books, and experiences have informed your view of the ocean?

3. If the environment were to get equal reporting and attention as the economy, would things be different? Explain.

4. Do the health risks attributed to climate change in developing countries concern you? Would you be more likely to change your lifestyle if you saw these effects firsthand rather than reading about them?

5. How well is your community preparing for the health impacts of climate change? What actions should it be taking?

6. What is the government's role in terms of promoting health? How do you view your role: conscious consumer, active citizen, community organizer, as an example to others?

7. When have you experienced the "healing powers" of nature?

8. Scott Russell Sanders describes his son's feelings of despair over the ecological crisis we face and his own practice of choosing hope. What gives you hope?

9. Share an insight from this week's EcoChallenge.

Weekly EcoChallenge: Saving Energy

Turn it down! Choose a realistic but challenging way to reduce your contribution to climate change by conserving energy. Locate the vampire appliances in your house that continually draw energy (coffee makers and toasters are good examples) and unplug them — or connect them to a power strip you can turn off. Take it further and plan an "energy fast" for an evening.

To find out more about NWEI's annual EcoChallenge event, visit www.ecochallenge.org

SUGGESTED READINGS AND RESOURCES

ORGANIZATIONS

350.org was founded by writer and activist Bill McKibben. Its mission is to inspire the world to rise to the challenge of the climate crisis — to create a new sense of urgency and of possibility for our planet.

FOUR YEARS.GO. is a campaign to catalyze and empower a fundamental shift in the direction of humanity. Fouryears.go.org. Watch their inspring three-minute video, "A Campaign to Change the Course of History," on their homepage or at www.youtube.com/watch?v=B_6iTCo5Ci8.

ARTICLES

Please go to the Northwest Earth Institute website (www.nwei.org) for the most current list of articles relating to this session.

BOOKS

Sustaining Life: How Human Health Depends on Biodiversity by Eric Chivian, M.D. and Aaron Bernstein, M.D., M.P.H. is a comprehensive, up-to-date work on the relationship between human health and the health of the living world.

Ten Ways to Change the World in Your Twenties, by Libuse Binder (2009). This book provides an inspiring collection of ideas that can make the world a better place. It provides resources and opportunities for twenty somethings to use their talents to help create a history we can all be proud of.

FILMS/DOCUMENTARIES

"End of the Line" (2009) explores the dangers of overfishing, not just to individual species of fish, but on the entire ocean ecosystem. For more information visit, www.endoftheline.com.

"Home" (2009). This online movie provides an overview of the earth's natural beauty and intricate interworkings and details the ways in which humanity is currently upsetting this beauty and balance, potentially irreversibly. Check out www.home-2009.com.

THINK LIKE AN OCEAN

By Andi McDaniel

My uncle Bill calls it "getting snarfed" — that unforgettable experience of being swept up by a huge wave, thrashed around like dirty laundry, and then spat onto the beach with a mouth full of saltwater and three pounds of sand in your pants. It's one way to contemplate the power of the ocean.

Me, I prefer to enjoy the ocean from the shore, where I can gaze out at it, in all of its vastness, and revel in just how little I know about this big, blue, complicated Earth. Given the countless environmental problems wrought by humans on land, I've always taken comfort in the ocean's size and complexity, as though those qualities made it less vulnerable to human meddling.

Sadly, I've begun to learn just how vulnerable the ocean really is. In 2003, *Nature* reported that, due to industrial fishing, only 10 percent of large fish remain in our oceans. Add to that the problems of mercury pollution, dead zones, coral bleaching, and acidification, and the oceans arguably are worse off than their terrestrial counterparts.

Which raises the question, why aren't we all freaking out about it?

One explanation is that the ocean's problems are hard to see. The surface isn't turning weird colors or becoming any less luminous for the devastation that lurks beneath. Nor is it assaulting our other senses, the way toxic dumps and smoggy city skies do.

Beyond even those reasons is the simple fact that humans are a land species. Necessarily, our concept of the ocean is based more on shows on the Discovery Channel than actual experience. And despite any harrowing statistics we might hear, we still picture that underwater wonderland teeming with colorful fish.

But land is deeply embedded in our psyches. It's land that stars in our historic cultural narratives, like *The Grapes of Wrath* and *Little House on the Prairie*. It's pride in land that fuels the quest for the great American lawn. And it's America's national parks — not its marine sanctuaries — that many consider our greatest environmental accomplishment.

Lately, millions of well-intentioned shoppers have begun to connect the food they buy with the land from which it comes. They read the fine print on their vegetables, meat, and dairy to assure themselves that their purchase will benefit the iconic farmer, cow, and beautiful pasture featured on the label. What could feel more wholesome than helping out these friendly, familiar characters, so central to our concept of America?

It's harder to identify with tuna.

And yet, mysterious though they may be, our oceans sustain us. As renowned marine biologist Sylvia Earle says, "Without the ocean, life on earth would simply not be possible. Should we care about the ocean? Do we care about living?" All told, the health of the oceans affects our livelihood as much as our farms and forests do. The connection just isn't as apparent.

Which is why the future of our oceans will depend upon the power of our imagination. As was the case when we learned about the hole in the ozone layer, ocean conservation requires us to reach beyond what we know to protect that which we can hardly comprehend.

If we don't address the crisis of our oceans, all of our other environmental efforts could be for naught. But unlike our efforts to preserve land, if the oceans are to heal, we'll need to be stewards of more than our immediate surroundings.

The ocean is not anyone's third-generation farmland, or favorite place to take nature walks, or even a fondly remembered childhood haunt. Yet, how we respond to the crisis of our oceans could determine what comes next in this Choose Your Own Adventure story we call life on Earth.

Published in the May/June 2007 issue of *Orion*. Andi McDaniel is a writer, journalist, and multimedia producer now living in the Twin Cities.

EMBEDDED IN NATURE:
HUMAN HEALTH AND BIODIVERSITY

By Eric Chivian, M.D., and Aaron S. Bernstein, M.D., M.P.H.

A loss of global biodiversity, namely a reduction in the variety of life on Earth, is rarely given much attention by physicians or environmental scientists. Like most people, they do not spend much time thinking about their relationship to other life forms, and they generally act, unknowingly, as if human beings were separate from the rest of nature — as if we could change the composition of the atmosphere and degrade the land and the oceans without these alterations having much effect on us. It is this disconnect that is at the core of the global environmental crisis — that policy makers and the public, by and large, do not understand that their health and their lives are ultimately dependent on other species and on the integrity of the planet's ecosystems, and as a result, they do not appreciate the urgent need to protect the natural world.

Approximately 1.7 million species have been identified on Earth and given Linnaen names (United Nations Environment Programme 1996), but there may be 10 times that number in all, and perhaps many times more if we include microbial diversity. Species interact with each other and with their physical and chemical environments to make up ecosystems such as forests and wetlands. Stratospheric ozone depletion, pollution, the introduction of alien species, the overharvesting of species and, increasingly, global climate change, all threaten biodiversity, and thus, ecosystem function. However, the degradation, reduction and fragmentation of habitats on land, in fresh water, and in the oceans are the greatest threats. All of these factors are the result of human activity and are driven by unsustainable consumption, especially in the industrialized world, and rising human populations. Together, they have disrupted grassland, river, lake, coral reef, and other ecosystems at alarming levels, and have raised the rate of species extinction to 100 and by some estimates, even to 1,000 times natural background rates.

The loss of species deprives us of invaluable tools for biomedical research that provides insights into how human cells and organ systems function in health and illness, and precludes our developing important new medicines for currently untreatable human diseases. …

WHAT ARE ECOSYSTEM SERVICES?

An ecosystem is an array of living things (plants, animals, and microbes) and the physical and chemical environment with which they interact. Examples of ecosystems include forests, wetlands, grasslands, streams, and estuaries. Healthy ecosystems provide the conditions and processes that sustain human life. In addition to providing goods such as foods and medicines, ecosystems also provide us with services, such as purification of air and water, the binding of toxins, decomposition of wastes, mitigation of floods, moderation of storm surges, stabilization of landscapes, and regulation of climate. We tend to take these services for granted and do not generally recognize that we cannot live without them, nor can other life on this planet.

WHAT IS THE VALUE OF THESE SERVICES?

Healthy ecosystems deliver life-sustaining services for free, and in many cases on a scale so large and complex that humanity would find it practically impossible to substitute for them. With respect to complexity, we often do not know which species are necessary for the services to work, what numbers they must be present in, and whether there are "keystone" species for ecosystem services. Disruption of these natural services can have catastrophic effects. For example, if natural pest control services ceased or populations of bees and other pollinators crashed, there could be major crop failures. If the carbon cycle were badly disrupted, rapid climate change could threaten whole societies. From an economic standpoint, numerous examples illustrate that ecosystem services that have been diminished by human activities can be restored for a fraction of the cost of building artificial substitutes. New York City's water quality was deteriorating due to development in the Catskill Mountains where the city's water supply originates. The cost of a filtration plant to deal with the increasing sewage and agricultural runoff would have been U.S. $5 — 8 billion plus an annual operating cost of U.S. $300 — $500 million. Alternatively, a one-time expenditure of U.S. $1.5 billion was able to restore the integrity of the watershed's natural purification services by purchasing and halting development on land in the Catskills, compensating landowners for restrictions on private development, and subsidizing improvement of septic systems.

Published in *Biodiversity: Its Importance to Human Health*, edited by Eric Chivian, M.D., founder and director, the Center for Health and the Global Environment, Harvard Medical School.

The importance of biodiversity to human health is particularly well illustrated by some human infectious diseases. Lyme disease, the most common vectorborne disease in the United States, is a prime example. When high levels of vertebrate-species diversity exist in a Lyme disease area, the risk of getting Lyme disease is lessened. One reason is that some of the vertebrates that are bitten by infected ticks, the vectors who transmit the Lyme bacteria, are "dead end" hosts — poorly able or incapable of passing on the bacteria and continuing the disease cycle. This effectively "dilutes" the disease agent and makes it less likely for an infected tick to transmit the disease to a human. Another reason this diversity is beneficial is that some vertebrate species compete with the main Lyme reservoir host or carrier (the white-foot mouse in the eastern United States), whereas others are predators — in both cases keeping mice populations low and reducing disease risk. This buffering effect conferred by biodiversity may also apply to other human infectious diseases such as West Nile encephalitis, cutaneous and visceral leishmaniasis, African trypanosomiasis, and Chagas disease.

Finally, and most importantly, ecosystems provide the life support systems for all life, including human life, on Earth. Not only do they give us food and fuel, but ecosystems, among other things, purify air and fresh water, bind and detoxify poisonous substances, break down wastes and recycle nutrients on land and in the oceans, pollinate crops and natural vegetation, make soils fertile, and store carbon, mitigating human-caused climate change. We tend to take these services for granted and generally do not recognize that we cannot live without them. Nor do we understand many ecosystem services well enough to re-create them, not knowing what species are necessary for the services to work and in what proportions, or whether for some services there are essential or "keystone" species without which ecosystems would cease to function. Human activity may now be altering some ecosystems in destructive ways that we are unaware of and that could lead to a collapse of their functioning.

The importance of recognizing how biodiversity affects human health and how it is increasingly threatened by human activity will only increase in coming years. Physicians and environmental scientists will need to understand these interconnections because they will be called upon to explain them to policy makers and the public. Such knowledge will also be critically important in clinical medicine, particularly in relation to the emergence and spread of some human infectious diseases.

Published in *Environmental Health Perspectives*, January 2004. Eric Chivian, M.D., is founder and director of the Center for Health and the Global Environment at Harvard Medical School. Aaron S. Bernstein, M.D., M.P.H., teaches at the University of Chicago Pritzker School of Medicine.

CLIMATE CHANGE AND HEALTH VULNERABILITIES

By Juan Almendares and Paul R. Epstein

Climate change has multiple direct and indirect consequences for human health — all of which are important. Climate change also threatens to disrupt Earth's life-support systems that underlie health and well-being. After all, human health and well-being basically depend on the health of crop systems, forests, other animals, and marine life. Health is the final common pathway for environmental and social conditions. Thus, the well-documented threats that climate change holds for societies and for ecosystems — for coral reefs, forests, and agriculture — ultimately pose the greatest long-term threats to health, nutrition, and well-being.

One of the first direct and most obvious results of climate change — an outcome clearly tied to rising average temperatures — is heat waves. These are expected to take an increasing toll in all nations. The disproportionate increase in nighttime temperatures since 1970 and the rising humidity that stems from warming oceans and a heated atmosphere increase the health threats from heat waves.

Extreme weather events, especially heavy downpours, can create conditions conducive to "clusters" of diseases carried by mosquitoes, rodents, and water. In addition, more intense hurricanes, droughts, and sea level rise are all projected to increase substantially the number of refugees and internally displaced persons across the globe — conditions that will squeeze resources (like water and food) and raise the risk of epidemics of communicable diseases.

Intense storms have other, less obvious effects on health. When Hurricane Mitch hit Central America in October 1998, it deposited six feet of rain in three days, causing flooding, landslides, and mudslides, and it dislodged pesticide-laden soils from banana, sugarcane and African palm plantations as well as sediments from ancient Mayan ruins. Areas surrounding gold mines became heavily contaminated with toxic chemicals and heavy metals, and surveys of the local population have shown a dramatic rise in skin and eye diseases. Along with causing 11,000 deaths, Mitch brought epidemics of malaria, dengue fever, cholera and leptospirosis. The damage continues to affect development in Honduras today.

Warming also expands the potential range of infectious diseases and disease carriers. In southern Honduras, the warming has been so great that mosquitoes infected with malaria no longer circulate. But people have also found the temperatures inhospitable and have moved north into forested areas ripe with malaria; so the indirect impact of climate change is that more people are exposed to health threats. Insect pests can affect not just humans, but also forests and crops, as well as livestock and wildlife.

To deal with these escalating problems, health care systems must be supported and public health services strengthened. Needed environmental measures include ecologically sound control of vector-borne diseases, such as malaria and dengue fever. Community research on the prevention of malaria has demonstrated that integrated control can be achieved without using DDT. The measures needed include community participation and training, treatment of infected populations, and larval control of anopheline mosquitoes.

Such solutions require organizing communities and mobilizing international forces to address these vital problems. Education is an essential component of all solutions. The development of schools that are ecologically sustainable in Colombia, El Salvador, Honduras, and Guatemala by Friends of the Earth International has helped in the search for appropriate solutions to climate change and health problems. Organic, locally grown agriculture promotes health and nutrition — the basis of resistance to disease.

The bottom line is that health must again take center stage and — as it did in the nineteenth and early twentieth centuries, when vast improvements in basic water and sanitation were made — become the cornerstone of clean, healthy and sustainable development.

Published in *State of the World 2009*, www.worldwatch.org. Dr. Juan Almendares is Physiology Professor at the Medical School, Universidad Nacional Autonoma de Honduras. Dr. Paul R. Epstein is the Associate Director of the Center for Health and the Global Environment at Harvard Medical School.

SPECIAL CONCERNS FOR COMMUNITIES AT HIGH RISK FOR HEALTH CONSEQUENCES OF CLIMATE CHANGE

Some Americans are particularly vulnerable to the negative consequences of climate change to health, including increasing heat stress, air pollution, extreme weather events, and disease carried by food, water and insects. These vulnerable populations include:

- Infants and children
- Pregnant women
- The poor
- The elderly
- Racial and ethnic minorities
- People with disabilities
- People with chronic medical conditions, including the obese
- Outdoor workers

Source: "Health Problems Heat Up: Climate Change and the Public's Health" www.HealthyAmericans.org

RESTORING NATURE, RESTORING YOURSELF

By Francesca Lyman

For a man broken by war, John Beal found himself an unlikely place of refuge. Hamm Creek was an open sewer, plugged up with garbage.

The disabled Vietnam veteran hadn't known where to turn. Told that he had less than four months to live and advised by his doctor to find a hobby to take his mind off his pain and suffering, he wandered down to the stream behind his house to contemplate his future. He stood on the shores of a backwater tributary of the Duwamish River, a dredged shipping channel on the outskirts of Seattle, edged by concrete factories and laced with toxic waste.

He was still recovering from bullet wounds and haunted by flashbacks. Besides suffering from post-traumatic stress disorder, he had gone through three heart attacks, followed by a serious motorcycle accident.

"I went down to the stream behind my house and just cried, wondering how I'd care for my wife and four kids," says Beal. "Then the idea came to me: If you're going to check out, so to speak, try to leave this place better than it was

when you found it. I looked at this wreck of a stream, filled with refrigerators, computers, old tires, torn garbage bags, broken swing sets, and stinking carpets, and all I wanted to do was clean it up."

Maybe it was a way of processing his memories of the wreckage of war, he admits. Maybe it was survivor's guilt. Or maybe his doctor's advice propelled him. Instead of despairing, he started simply pulling out the garbage. "When I yanked out this huge refrigerator, I thought it would surely kill me. Instead I felt better."

Since that day 23 years ago, Beal has directed all of his energies to cleaning up and restoring this polluted stream flowing out of Seattle's industrial south end. During the last ten years he has moved on to restoring the entire watershed of which it is a part.

"John really deserves credit for realizing that the Duwamish River and its estuaries could be restored to health, at a time when many people had written off the urbanized Duwamish as a lost cause," says Kathy Fletcher, executive director of The People for Puget Sound, a citizen's organization that involves local citizens in protecting and restoring local streams.

Beal has recruited hundreds of crews to clean up and replant around the streams and has now established a network of volunteer groups living in the area, as well as drawing the support and interest of the local Duwamish tribe.

Through sheer persistence, and with the help of groups like People for Puget Sound, Beal eventually raised enough public awareness and pressure to persuade the local utility to allow Hamm Creek, which had been channelized and paved into a culvert, to be daylighted and rerouted over its property.

"The most dramatic thing is how quickly the creek began reviving," Fletcher says, adding that within days of a huge effort to daylight and replant the area little salmonids began appearing. What was once a culvert dripping with waste is now a beautifully recontoured and replanted stream brimming with beaver, salmon, and other fish.

For Beal, the impulse to do environmental restoration is itself restorative: "It has empowered me and kept me alive." That same impulse has spurred the energies of thousands of volunteers. "I've seen remarkable things happen to people who connect with Mother Earth," he concludes, describing dozens of cases of people disabled physically or psychologically who benefit from the exercise and feeling of accomplishment. "They see a light go on when they get here."

"I remember watching a young man who had been in a wheelchair for eight years come out to help us weed and plant," he says. "After two years, he's almost able to walk." At first, the disabled man would fall out of his wheelchair, Beal recalls. But now, he says, the man is able to clamber down the slope of the shore, willing himself through. "He was out there every single day. And lately he's saying, 'Now I've got a mission in life.'"

No matter how stressed, angry, depressed or troubled they are, whether it's a jail crew sent to clean up litter for the day or a class of disabled students, they seem to derive pleasure from the activity, says the riverkeeper.

The redemptive feelings Beal describes are echoed by thousands of visitors and volunteers who have come to his restored creeksite. They are also confirmed by an emerging movement loosely called "ecopsychology," the study of nature's therapeutic benefits.

Look around, says Michael Cohen, founder of a hands-on wilderness therapy course called Project Nature Connect. People long to be put back into nature, crave having their lives fit into some ancient order. For evidence, one need look no further than the widespread reaction of Americans in the wake of the September 11 terror attacks, he notes. Compelled to go to a place that would ease their shock and sadness, many instinctively flocked to city parks, flower gardens, overlooks, and other natural areas.

Nothing could have been less surprising to John Beal. After the September 11 attacks, he recalls turning to his wife and saying, "Hamm Creek's going to be a lot busier now. The entire US will be going through post-traumatic stress disorder."

In the last decade, hundreds of studies have begun documenting what many people know intuitively about the healing power of nature. "Nature is in some fundamental way important for the human psyche, and as such it is really central to public health," says Roger Ulrich, director of the Center for Health Systems and Design at Texas A&M University. A pioneer in the field, Ulrich has tested these theories on patients recovering from cardiac and abdominal surgery. He found that patients whose hospital rooms overlooked trees required less pain medication and recovered more quickly than those whose rooms overlooked brick walls.

John Beal, like the ecopsychologists, believes that the impulse toward environmental restoration is about the need for connection and purpose in a world increasingly disassociated from nature. "It's the connection to something larger than yourself," says Beal. "When you are so overwhelmed by your depression, or anxiety or sense of illness, it takes away that worry; it calms that fear."

This article originally appeared in the Spring 2003 edition of *Yes! Magazine*. Francesca Lyman also writes the "Your Environment" column for MSNBC online.

THREE BETS

By Sandra Steingraber

Thirty years ago, in between my sophomore and junior years of college, I was diagnosed with bladder cancer. Those are amazing words to write: *Thirty years ago I had cancer. I had just turned twenty.* I was hoping that I would live long enough to have sex with someone; I hadn't done that yet. I could not have imagined, while lying in my hospital bed, exhaling anesthesia, that someday I could write, *Thirty years ago I had cancer.*

Last fall, on a sunny afternoon, the phone rang while I was trying to meet a writing deadline. It was the nurse in my urologist's office. She was calling to say that the pathologist had found, in the urine collected from my last cystoscopic checkup, abnormal cell clusters. And also blood.

After I hung up, I looked out the window of my small house where the sun still shone on the last of the marigolds and tomato vines. I looked down at my computer screen where the cursor still blinked on the same paragraph. I could hear in the kitchen the tomatoes still bobbing around in the stockpot that was steaming away on the stove. The world was still the same, but it felt to me a suddenly altered place.

I provided a second urine sample for further testing, and based on the results of that, a third sample that was sent out for genetic analysis. Ten days later, I got a call from the urology nurse. The results were normal.

So what am I trying to say here? Am I fine or not fine? Well, I don't know. I'm living within that period of time known as watchful waiting. Much of my adult life has been one of watchful waiting. *Watchful* means vigilance, screening tests, imaging, blood work, self-advocacy, second opinions, and hours logged in hospital parking garages. *Waiting* means you go back to your half-finished essay, to the tomatoes on the stove. You lay plans and carry on within the confines of ambiguity. You meet deadlines and make grocery lists. And sometimes you jump when the phone rings on a sunny afternoon.

Thirty years ago I had cancer.

After I left the hospital, I went back to the university, resumed my life as a biology major, and began mucking around in the medical literature. It didn't take me too long to learn that bladder cancer is considered a quintessential environmental cancer, meaning that we have more evidence for a link between toxic chemical exposures and bladder cancer risk than for almost any other kind of cancer, with data going back a hundred years. I also discovered that the identification of bladder carcinogens does not preclude their ongoing use in commerce. Just because, through careful scientific study, we learn that a chemical causes cancer doesn't mean that we ban it from the marketplace.

I also learned that, in spite of all this evidence, the words *carcinogen* and *environment* rarely appeared in the pamphlets on cancer in my doctors' offices and waiting rooms. Nor were these words used much in conversations I had with my various health-care providers, who were interested instead in my family medical history. I was happy enough to provide it. There is a lot of cancer in my family. My mother was diagnosed with breast cancer at age forty-four. I have uncles with colon cancer, prostate cancer, stromal cancer. My aunt died of the same kind of bladder cancer — transitional cell carcinoma — that I had.

But here's the punch line to my family story: I am adopted. I'm not related to my family by chromosomes. So I began to ask hard questions about the presumption that what runs in families must necessarily run in genes. I began to ask, what else do families have in common? Such as, say, drinking water wells. And when I looked at the literature on cancer among adult adoptees, I learned that, in fact, the chance of an adopted person dying of cancer is closely related to whether or not her adoptive parents had died of cancer and far less related to whether or not her biological parents had met such a fate. But you would never know that based on the questions asked on medical intake forms.

So thirty years ago, as a college undergraduate, I made a bet. I bet that my cancer diagnosis had something to do with the environment in which I lived as a child. And I think I was right about this.

As I learned years later, while researching my book *Living Downstream*, the county where I grew up, along the east bluff of the Illinois River, has statistically elevated cancer rates. Three dozen different industries line the river valley there, and farmers practice chemically intensive agriculture along its floodplains. Hazardous waste is imported from as far away as New Jersey, and the drinking water wells contain traces of both farm chemicals and industrial chemicals, including those with demonstrable links to . . . bladder cancer.

Twenty years ago, in the fall of 1988, when I was a graduate student in biology at the University of Michigan, I made another bet. I was working as an opinion writer at the *Michigan Daily*, the student newspaper there. My editor and I laid bets as to which system would collapse first — economy or ecology. I said ecology. I think I was wrong.

I think we were both wrong. They seem to be crumbling simultaneously.

Let's compare our twin "eco" systems. Our economy and our ecology have in common, it seems to me, a number of shared attributes. Both are complex, globalized systems whose interconnections are little understood until something goes wrong. Who knew that mortgages in California could lead to bankruptcy in Iceland? But there it is. Who knew that the miracle of pollination depends on the synchronicity of time and temperature? But the ongoing decoupling of day length — which awakens the flowers — from ambient temperature — which awakens the bees — reveals that it is so dependent.

In both systems, eroding diversity creates fragility, as when financial systems merge and collapse, as when farming systems become monocultures and thereby vulnerable to catastrophic pest outbreaks. Damage to both systems is made worse by positive feedback loops. In the economic world, panic and fear drive investment decisions that lead to more panic and fear. In the ecological

protect the planet

Thanks to the Earth Institute of West Michigan

world, greenhouse gases raise temperatures that melt permafrost. Melted permafrost rots and releases more greenhouse gases.

Here's a key difference, though. For one of our failing ecosystems, we became immediately engaged in drastic and unprecedented measures to rescue it — even though no one seemed to understand it very well. And for our other ecosystem ... well, it's still widely considered too depressing and overwhelming to talk about in much detail.

As part of my work, I visit a lot of college campuses. Lately, I've been asking students to engage in a thought exercise: Imagine that ecological metrics were as familiar to us as economic ones. Imagine ecological equivalents to the Dow, NASDAQ, and S&P that reported to us every day — in newspapers, on radio, on websites, on the crawl at the bottom of TV screens, on oversized tickers in Times Square — data about the various sectors of our ecological system and how they are faring. What are the atmospheric parts per million of carbon dioxide today? Has the extinction rate become inflationary? What is the exchange rate between sea ice and fresh water? What is the national deficit of topsoil?

Now imagine that the mainstream media were as interested in the thoughts of the president's ecological team — most notably marine biologist Jane Lubchenco, who now leads the National Oceanic and Atmospheric Administration, and climate expert John Holdren, the president's new science advisor — as they are in the opinions of his economic team. Imagine if, in primetime interview after interview, these public servants provided us regular environmental analysis. On an almost daily basis, the American citizenry would be reminded that one in every four mammals now appears to be heading toward extinction. The Gulf Stream, which drives nutrient cycling in our oceans, is starting to get wobbly, while dead zones in the oceans are growing. The oceans, we would be informed, provide half of our planetary oxygen. Shoveling coal into ovens to generate electricity is loading the atmosphere with mercury, which rains down and is transformed by ancient bacteria into the powerful brain poison methylmercury.

Methylmercury is siphoned up the food chain, concentrating as it goes, so that nearly all freshwater lakes and streams east of the Mississippi are now unfishable, and we must advise women and children against eating tuna salad sandwiches.

Imagine that all Americans find out, whether they want

to or not, that atmospheric loading of carbon dioxide is acidifying the ocean in ways that, if unchecked, will drop pH to the point where calcium carbonate goes into solution, and that will spell the end of anything with a shell — from clams and oysters to coral reefs.

Suppose that ecological pundits discussed every night on cable TV the ongoing disappearance of bees, bats, and other pollinators and the possibly dire consequences for our food supply. Suppose we received daily reports on the status of our aquifers. Suppose legislators and citizens both agreed that if we don't take immediate action to bail out our ecological system, something truly terrible will happen. Our ecology will tank.

The fact that nothing close to this is happening is the difference between economy and ecology, both of which share an etymology: *eco*, from the Greek *oikos*, meaning "household."

Ten years ago, I gave birth to a child. After twenty years as a solitary adult ecologist, I became a habitat, an inland ocean with a marine mammal swimming around inside of me. I became a water cycle. A food chain. A jet stream. My daughter's name is Faith. I'll leave it to you to imagine why an adopted cancer survivor might name a daughter Faith. My daughter is planning a career as a marine biologist. She wants to write her first book on the octopus. My son Elijah is seven. He is named for the abolitionist Elijah Lovejoy, who hails from my home state of Illinois. Elijah wishes to be the president, a farmer, or a member of the Beatles. He figures there are two job openings there already.

Since becoming a mother, I've made another bet. I am betting that, in between my own adult life and my children's, an environmental human rights movement will arise. It's one whose seeds have already been sown, and it's one with a dual focus. First, the environmental human rights movement will take up with urgency the task of rescuing and repairing our ecological system upon which all human life depends. It is a movement that will recognize the truth of the following statement: "Nothing is more important to human beings than an ecologically functioning, life sustaining biosphere on the Earth. ... We cannot live long or well without a functioning biosphere, and so it is worth everything we have." Those are the opening sentences of a powerful new manifesto, "Law for the Ecological Age," authored by attorney and biochemist Joseph Guth and published in the *Vermont Journal of Environmental Law*.

At the same time, this environmental human rights

> "Nothing is more important to human beings than an ecologically functioning, life sustaining biosphere on earth... We cannot live long or well without a functioning biosphere, and so it is worth everything we have"

Thanks to an anonymous donor

movement will take up with equal fervor the task of divorcing our economy from its current dependencies on chemical toxicants that are known to trespass inside our bodies, without our consent, thus violating, as some have argued, our security of person. Our current environmental regulatory apparatus does not require rigorous toxicological testing of chemicals as a precondition for marketing them, as we do, for example, for pharmaceuticals. It also makes it very difficult to ban chemicals once they are in commerce. Of the eighty thousand synthetic chemicals allowed into the market, exactly five have been outlawed under the Toxics Substances Control Act since 1976. Our current environmental regulatory apparatus allows economic benefits to be balanced against human health risks. It fails to take into account the fact that we are all exposed, to use Rachel Carson's words, to a changing kaleidoscope of chemicals over our lifetimes and not just one chemical at a time.

In umbilical cord blood alone, 287 different chemicals have been identified, including pesticides, stain removers, wood preservatives, mercury, and flame retardants. Our current environmental regulatory apparatus does not take into account the timing of exposure. And yet the science clearly shows that toxic exposures during key moments of infant and child development — especially during the opera of embryonic development — raise risks for harm in ways that are not predictable by dose. Benzo[a]pyrene, an ingredient in tobacco smoke, diesel exhaust, and soot, can damage eggs in the ovaries. Exposure to pesticides in men can reduce sperm count. Thus, our environmental policies may be eroding our fertility. And if a pregnancy is achieved, exposure to certain chemicals raises the risk that it will be lost through miscarriage, or what we in the scientific community call spontaneous abortion. Evidence suggests that the pesticide methoxchlor has this power, as do certain chemical solvents.

And here is where I am interested in engaging the pro-life community in dialogue, because whether you see this problem, as I do, as a violation of women's reproductive rights, or whether you see this problem, as many members of my own family do, as a violation of fetal sanctity, maybe we can all agree, pro-life and pro-choice, that any chemical with the power to extinguish human pregnancy has no rightful place in our economy.

When toxic chemicals enter the story of human development during the fifth and sixth months of pregnancy, when the brain is just getting itself knitted together, the risk may be a learning or developmental disability. Of the 3,000 chemicals produced in high volume in the United States, 200 are neurotoxicants and another 1,000 are suspected of affecting the nervous system.

Some chemicals, such as PCBs, have the power to shorten human gestation and so raise the risk for premature birth, which is the leading cause of disability in this country. After birth, some chemicals, such as certain air pollutants, can retard the development of the lungs in ways that impede later athletic performance. Some chemicals raise the risk for pediatric cancers, which are rising in incidence more rapidly than cancers among adults.

Some chemicals can raise the risk for early puberty in girls, which in turn raises the risk for breast cancer in adulthood. In short, chemical toxicants can sabotage the story of child development and so make urgent the need for restructuring our chemicals policy along the principles of precaution and green design. But toxic chemicals do not only discriminate against children, they may also

Thanks to Stephen Shostek and Jacqi Tull

discriminate against our elders. New evidence links environmental exposures to neurotoxicants to increased risks of dementing disorders in old age.

So I am betting that chemical reform will be a cornerstone of this new environmental human rights movement that I see getting under way. I am betting that my children — and the generation of children they are a part of — will, by the time they are my age, consider it unthinkable to allow cancer-causing chemicals, reproductive toxicants, and brain-destroying poisons to freely circulate in our economy. They will find it unthinkable to assume an attitude of silence and willful ignorance about our ecology.

In the same way, I look back on the life of Rachel Carson — my mentor in all this, who died when I was five years old — and find it unthinkable that she could not speak about her own cancer diagnosis, even while dying, as I have written about my diagnosis here. Thirty years of feminism lies between my life as an adult scientist and Rachel Carson's. That human rights movement has ended the silence around the personal experience of cancer so that I have never had to fear, as did Carson, that my status as a cancer survivor will be used to impeach my science.

And in the same way, I look back on the life of Abraham Lincoln, whose portrait hangs in every schoolroom in Illinois, and marvel that our economy was once dependent on slave labor. Unthinkable. I believe our grandchildren will look back on us and marvel that our economy was once dependent on chemicals that were killing the planet and killing ourselves.

Now I am willing to concede the point that this environmental human rights movement that I am betting on is less an evidence-based prediction than a mother's fervent hope that my children will never have to fear that the phone ringing on a sunny afternoon will bring bad news from the pathology lab. I'm willing to admit that this bet is a wish that my children will grow up in a world with a functioning Gulf Stream, and some ice caps, and a few coral reefs. And some octopi for my daughter to write her first book about. And some honeybees to help my son the farmer grow apples. It's a wish that his polar bear Halloween costume not outlast the species.

Wishful or not, I am determined to win this bet because my children's lives are inextricably bound to the abiding ecology of this planet, which is worth everything I could possibly wager. An environmental human rights movement is the vision under which I labor, from which I am not free to desist, and which may, if we all work together, become a self-fulfilling prophecy.

May it be so.

Published in the May/June 2009 issue of *Orion*. Sandra Steingraber is a scholar in residence in the Division of Interdisciplinary and International Studies at Ithaca College, and the author of *Having Faith*. Her latest work is a documentary entitled *Living Downstream*.

EXCERPT FROM
HUNTING FOR HOPE

By Scott Russell Sanders

More than a year has gone by since Jesse and I built a fire in the rain, but the notebook I carried on that mountain journey still smells of wood smoke. More than two years have passed since we quarreled in the Rockies, but his words about the need for hope still ring in my head as if he had just quit speaking. "You've got me seeing nothing but darkness," he tells me, his voice cracking with pain. "I have to believe there's a way we can get out of this mess. Otherwise what's the point? Why study, why work, why do anything if it's all going to hell?"

I cannot scour from my vision the darkness that troubles my son, because I have witnessed too much suffering and waste, I know too much about what humans are doing to one another and to the planet. I cannot answer Jesse's questions about hope, or Eva's, or those of my students, by pretending that I see no reasons for despair. Anyone who pays attention to the state of the world knows that we are in trouble. Anyone who looks honestly at the human prospect realizes that we face enormous challenges: population growth, environmental degradation, extinction of species, ethnic and racial strife, doomsday weapons, epidemic disease, drugs, poverty, hunger, and crime, to mention only a few. These stark realities press on my mind as I write. What

I have been saying in this book is that they are not the only realities, nor the most powerful or durable ones. I see light shining in the darkness. I live in hope.

"What's the good of grieving if you can't change anything?" Jesse demanded of me during our quarrel in the Rocky Mountains. A year later, amidst the rushing of streams in the Smokies, he put the question more calmly but no less intently: "Do you believe we can change? That we're not stuck in this dead-end way of thinking?"

I answered yes that day; I am answering yes now. My search for hope has convinced me that we can change our ways of seeing and thinking and living. We can begin living responsibly and alertly right where we are, right now, no matter how troubled we may be about the human prospect. If we set out to solve the world's problems, we are likely to feel overwhelmed. On the other hand, if we set out to act on our deepest concerns and conviction, we may do some good. We can begin making changes in our own lives without waiting for such changes to become popular, without knowing whether they will have any large-scale effect, but merely because we believe they are right.

For my part, I believe that all but the poorest of us could choose to lead materially simpler lives, and thereby do less harm and reap more joy. We could learn to be guided by what we need rather than by what the hucksters urge us to want. We could ignore fashion and hype, and look for true quality — in products, services, art, and people. We could work toward a more just distribution of wealth, within our own country and among nations. We could re-imagine ourselves as conservers rather than consumers — conservers of land and air and water and all the earth's bounty, conservers of human achievements from the past and human potential for the future, conservers of beauty and wildness.

If we are determined to live in hope, we could make a more serious commitment to sustaining our families, recognizing that, in spite of all their flaws, they are the best means we have for nurturing children and fostering love. We could re-imagine ourselves as inhabitants rather than tourists, cultivating a stronger sense of place, learning about the land, its natural and human history, and the needs of our communities. We could decide to stay put, in our houses and neighborhoods, unless we have compelling reasons to move. We could think hard before we jump in a car or an airplane and zoom off, making sure each trip is worth what it costs the earth. Instead of rushing about, we could slow down, center down, and open ourselves to the five rivers of the senses.

We could learn to satisfy more of our own needs ourselves, with help from families and neighbors and friends. When we buy goods and services, we could give more of our business to local farmers, artists, craftspeople, skilled workers, merchants and manufacturers, and to locally owned enterprises, since people who share a place with us are more likely to care for it than strangers are. We could accept more graciously our responsibilities as citizens, informing ourselves about public matters, taking our turn at public service, honoring the necessity of government and making sure that our representatives govern well. In the inevitable clash of private interests, we could speak up for the common good.

As we transform our own lives, we join with others who are making a kindred effort, and thus our work will be multiplied a thousandfold across the country and a millionfold around the earth. Whether all such efforts, added together, will be enough to avert disaster and bring about a just and enduring way of life, no one can say. In order to live in hope we needn't believe that everything will turn out well. We need only believe that we are on the right path.

What endures? What lifts our hearts? What do we possess in abundance? For most of our history, we newcomers to America have imagined that animals, trees, water, soil, clean air are inexhaustible, when they are, in fact, limited and vulnerable. We have considered peace and prosperity and civil order to be our birthright, when they are, in fact, hard won and easily lost. Our truly abundant resources are mostly intangible, difficult to describe and impossible to measure, and among them are love, beauty, skill, compassion, community, fidelity, simplicity, and wildness. Through cruelty or carelessness we can destroy the conditions that nurture these powers, but the powers themselves are not used up in our experience of them.

This excerpt was taken from *Hunting for Hope: A Father's Journey* by Scott Russell Sanders, Beacon Press. 1999. Scott Russell Sanders' writing examines the human place in nature, the pursuit of social justice, the relation between culture and geography, and the search for a spiritual path.

Those who contemplate the beauty of the earth
find reserves of strength that will endure as long as life lasts.

— RACHEL CARSON, ECOLOGIST, AUTHOR OF *SILENT SPRING*

Thanks to Peter Englander

SESSION 6 — HEALTHY PLANET, HEALTHY SELF
WHAT YOU CAN DO

If after completing this week's EcoChallenge you are motivated to take further action, consider the suggestions listed below. At your group's final gathering, you will have an opportunity to review the list again and commit to an action item.

Label each of these action items with a code representing its priority in your life.

N: Will do now
S: Will do within the next month
L: Will do within the next year
N/A: Not applicable to me

BEGIN RIGHT AWAY:

____ Know where your products come from and value products originating closer to you

____ Eat lower on the food chain

____ Turn off lights when you leave a room

____ Unplug and reconnect with Earth

____ Lower your thermostat in the winter and raise it in the summer

____ Watch the 45 second video "You Have the Power: Save Energy" to gain a visual of greenhouse gas emissions our homes produce: www.youtube.com/watch?v=6Eg_SEAnE-M

____ Reduce and reuse, THEN recycle.

____ Other: _____

RESEARCH AND APPLY YOUR KNOWLEDGE:

____ Know where your energy comes from and choose the greenest option. Go to www.epa.gov/cleanenergy/energy-and-you

____ Know where your waste goes. Google "solid waste management" followed by your location

____ Learn what climate change means for your region. Go to www.epa.gov/climate change and click on "where you live"

____ Learn what restoration projects are happening in your community and lend a hand

____ Fly less: consider vacations closer to home or taking the train

____ Learn what teleconferencing options you can use

____ Calculate your carbon footprint to identify your biggest sources of greenhouse gas emissions and set individual or family goals to reduce them. Go to www.climatecare.org or to www.epa.gov/climatechange/emissions/ind_calculator.html

____ Other: _____

REQUIRES MORE RESOURCES (TIME, ENERGY, MONEY, PEOPLE):

____ Schedule a home energy audit and implement recommendations

____ Determine if solar panels are an option for your household

____ Hang your clothes out to dry

____ Attend a beach clean up. Go to www.oceanconservancy.org to learn more

____ Support conservation groups

____ Advocate for clean air, food and water for all

____ Organize a group to take the Northwest Earth Institute's *Reconnecting With Earth* course

____ Don't give up, choose hope

____ Other: _____

CALL TO ACTION

"The character of a whole society is the cumulative result of countless small actions, day in and day out, of millions of persons."

— Duane Elgin, author, *Voluntary Simplicity*

The final session is an opportunity to celebrate the completion of the course, reflect upon your experience and discuss future actions you can take individually and as a group. Most discussion groups choose to share a potluck meal together as they discuss their experience and decide what they will do next. Prior to this session, please make sure to complete the evaluation form on page 7 and bring it to the meeting.

Many participants would like the continued support of a group to help them make changes in their personal lives. We suggest you review the **What You Can Do** pages before you meet for this final session and choose one from each session (sessions 2 through 6 have lists) that you can commit to doing. Write them down in the space provided below. At your final meeting, you can take time to share your plans and determine how you will provide accountability and support to one another.

In addition to making changes in their lives, group members often want to work together on a project. Should your group feel motivated to take on a collective project, the What You Can Do pages provide some suggestions that are appropriate for groups as well. The following list offers other actions taken by groups that have completed NWEI courses:

• Schedule a monthly hike or group gathering to continue engaging with each other

• Take part in a beach clean-up or river restoration project.

• Schedule monthly work parties to help each other with house projects, gardening, etc.

• If members live near one another, brainstorm ways to carpool to common destinations.

• Attend a local or regional planning meeting to weigh in on environmental health issues.

• Tour a local waste facility to find out where your garbage goes. Next, find out where to recycle those items that cannot be placed in curbside containers and organize a joint weekly/monthly pick-up or drop-off.

• Join a CSA; split a share with another member if you can't use a whole share yourself.

• Start a letter writing campaign to leaders advocating for the changes you wish to see.

• Organize an event with a speaker or hold a film screening to promote awareness of environmental health issues. See NWEI's film recommendations listed under "Suggested Resources" in each session.

Once your group reaches a consensus about what project you'll undertake, create a specific follow-up plan and delegate responsibilities.

If you are interested in offering or participating in other NWEI discussion course programs, please visit www.nwei.org for a complete list of course offerings. At our website you can also support this work by becoming a member of the Northwest Earth Institute, joining our email list, and reading our blog. Thank you for your participation; we sincerely hope this discussion course was an enriching and inspiring experience for you!

Session	Action item	Time frame
Eating Well		
Cleaning House		
Building Healthy Communities		
Curing Consumption		
Healthy Planet, Healthy Self		

PERMISSIONS

MEMBERSHIP

Inspiring people to take responsibility for Earth.

Thank you for participating in this Northwest Earth Institute discussion course!

We hope that you found your experience to be meaningful and inspiring. If you would like to help others discover their role in fostering health and well-being, please consider joining NWEI as a member. Thanks to our members, we are able to reach communities across North America in an effort to create a sustainable future for us all.

To join, fax this form to (503) 227-2917 or mail it to Northwest Earth Institute, 107 SE Washington, Suite 235, Portland, OR 97214. You can also join online at www.nwei.org/join.

☐ **I'd like to make a donation to the Northwest Earth Institute.**

Name _____

Address _____

City _____ State _____ Zip code _____

Telephone: Day (_____) _____ Evening (_____) _____

Email address _____

Individual Membership (tax deductible):

☐ Regular $35
☐ Household/Contributor $50
☐ Earth Steward $100
☐ Sustainer $250
☐ Patron $500
☐ Founder's Circle $1,000

Please see our website or contact us for more information on member benefits for individual and business memberships.

☐ **I'm already a member. Here's an additional gift. $_____**

Pay by credit card: ☐ Visa   ☐ MasterCard

Card number _____ Expiration date_____

Signature _____

☐ **I would like information on how to offer a course on:**

☐ Menu for the Future   ☐ Discovering a Sense of Place   ☐ Voluntary Simplicity
☐ Global Warming: Changing CO$_2$urse ☐ Reconnecting With Earth   ☐ Sustainable Systems at Work
☐ Choices for Sustainable Living ☐ Healthy Children — Healthy Planet

Thank you for your support!

Northwest Earth Institute 107 SE Washington, Suite 235, Portland, OR 97214